D1360910

Geography . . . USA

Exploring the Five Themes

by Jerry Aten

illustrated by
Milton Hall

Notice! Copies of student pages may be reproduced by the classroom teacher for classroom use only, not for commercial resale. No part of this publication may be reproduced for storage in a retrieval system, or transmitted in any form or by any means–electronic, mechanical, recording, etc.–without the prior written permission of the publisher. Reproduction of these materials for an entire school or school system is strictly prohibited.

FS-10181 Geography . . . USA
All rights reserved–Printed in the U.S.A.
Copyright © 1995 Frank Schaffer Publications, Inc.
23740 Hawthorne Blvd.
Torrance, CA 90505

Table of Contents

HOW TO USE THIS BOOK

Many of the activities and teaching strategies found in this book are based on the five themes of geography. Those themes were created out of a call for improved instruction in geographic education and were first published in 1984 under the title of *Guidelines for Geographic Education*. This publication was the result of a joint effort by the National Council for Geographic Education and the Association of American Geographers.

Those five themes identified were *location, place, movement, regions,* and *interaction*. Their main purpose was to provide teachers with a definitive structure for teaching geography that would emphasize the legitimacy and importance of the subject and establish its relevance to the lives of students. An explanation of the five themes is found on the first two pages of this book.

While the organization of the material has been based around those five themes, it should be emphasized that seldom does an activity or teaching strategy involve only the use of a single theme. For example, how can we think of a place's specific *location* without thinking of the *place* itself and the characteristics that make it unique on its own? Likewise when we think of the *interaction* of human beings and their impact on the environment, it is impossible in a geographic sense to exclude the *location* (the "where") of that environment. Other examples could be cited, but the point is simply that the use of one theme often spills over into the use of another.

Several of the activities are based on placing students into pairs. The reason for this is to get them into a pattern of interacting with one another. Exchanging ideas and thoughts with others will help students to analyze and evaluate their own decisions and conclusions. Sharing thoughts with a larger group or even the entire class takes the issue a step further and will make the assignment more meaningful. Some of the questions and activities do require a specific correct answer. However, many were designed as thinking and conclusion-drawing activities that encourage students to develop and then explain their own line of thinking.

While stereotypical thinking should be avoided, students are encouraged to develop some general conclusions about specific areas of the United States. To conclude that skiing is important to the economy of the mountainous western states is not to suggest that everyone who lives there is an avid skier. Likewise to suggest that Mexican food is quite popular in the Southwest does not imply that seafood restaurants have little chance of success!

Following the five themes of geography, there is a unit on weather and climate. This unit is included because often it is the case that middle school students have very limited ideas about the kinds of weather patterns that are typical in other parts of the

7. How many national parks are located within the three states of Alaska, California, and Utah?_____

8. How many states have no national park?_____

9. Is there a national park (or parks) in your state? If not, choose a place within the boundaries of your state you feel would be a good candidate for becoming a national park someday. Explain your choice in the space below.

   _____

   _____

   _____

10. Choose one park that is of particular interest to you. Research its history, its size, and any other facts you find interesting. Summarize your findings in the space below and share with other members of your class.

   _____

   _____

   _____

   _____

   _____

   _____

   _____

   _____

   _____

   _____

   _____

   _____

   _____

   _____

   _____

United States Map

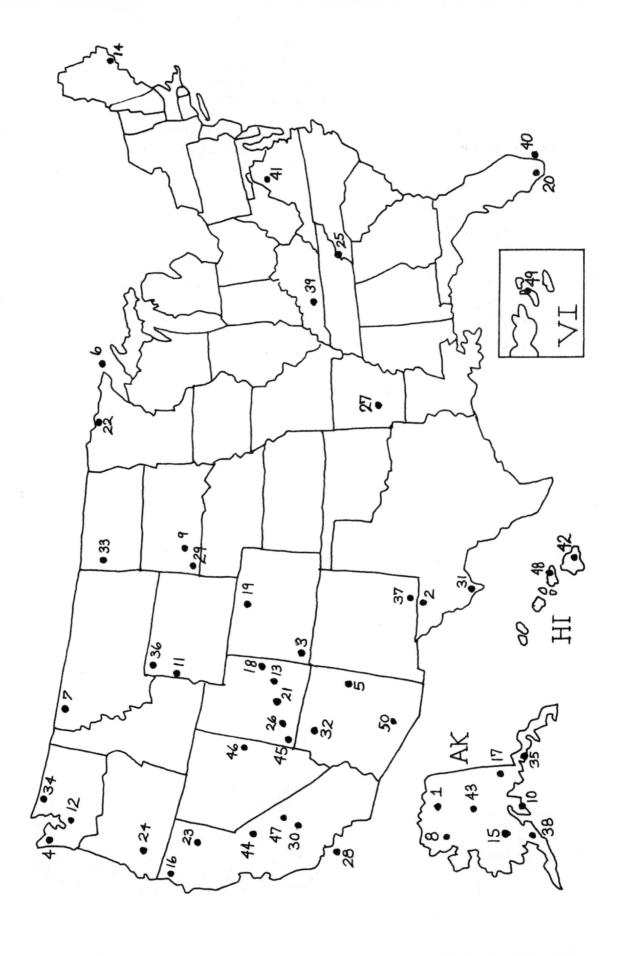

National Park Scramble

Below and on the next page are the names of our 50 national parks. The letters are all out of order. See how many parks you can identify by unscrambling the letters and writing the correct spelling in the space following the letters. Use the alphabetical list provided in the "A Legacy at Risk" activity to help you with the scramble.

1. GINKS ACYNNO _____
2. WEORODD _____
3. CYOKR INUMOATN _____
4. AWIIAH ELOVONCAS _____
5. CAAIAD _____
6. DRGNA NYACNO _____
7. YMLOIPA _____
8. NOIZ _____
9. IDNW CVEA _____
10. IQESOUA _____
11. EEHOOTDR LVORSOEET _____
12. HENOSANDAH _____
13. TM ARNREI _____
14. LSIE OYRELA _____
15. EYOVGURSA _____
16. NRIGIV NISDALS _____
17. AERGT ABISN _____
18. ERATCR KALE _____
19. SCHRAE _____
20. IBG NEBD _____

21. MAAIKT   _____

22. HMATOMM EACV   _____

23. AEMS ERVED   _____

24. EIAGLCR   _____

25. ELOLOEYTWNS   _____

26. LWRGALNE - ST. ILESA   _____

27. TSEOYIME   _____

28. IAKNE RJFODS   _____

29. SETAG OF HTE ACRCIT   _____

30. ALDBNDAS   _____

31. APICTOL EREF   _____

32. DNRGA OTTEN   _____

33. SSEALN CLAOVNIC   _____

34. TEIIEFPRD EOFTRS   _____

35. BUKOK LLEVAY   _____

36. YABCNIES   _____

37. AREEGVLDSE   _____

38. ICALGER AYB   _____

39. HLENACN LSAINSD   _____

40. NAYSNALCNOD   _____

41. AETRG YOMSK SIOUTMNAN   _____

42. ALEKAHAAL   _____

43. EKAL RLCAK   _____

44. ROHTN AACCSEDS   _____

45. TOH NRPSIGS   _____

46. LNEDAI   _____

47. ABSRALCD RVACENS   _____

48. YRCBE YNAOCN   _____

49. DPAALUGUE AUIONNMTS   _____

50. GORSAAU   _____

Have you ever been to a national park? If you have, list any parks you have visited in the space below. If you have never been to a national park, which one would you like to visit most?

_____

_____

_____

ADJACENT STATES

Divide the class into four or five teams with an equal number of students on each team. The teacher (or a student) will monitor the game and should have access to a good map of the United States. No other maps should be showing! The object of the game is to familiarize students with the locations of the states relative to their positions to one another.

The game begins with the teacher calling out the name of any state. For example, the teacher may say, "Colorado." Students then gather within their groups and determine among themselves the names of all those states that lie adjacent to Colorado. When a team is confident of its response, one of its members calls out, "Colorado!" It then becomes that team's state if it can correctly name all of those states that have boundaries touching Colorado.

The successful team will be awarded one point for each state named if and only if they correctly name all eight states that border Colorado. In the example, the states that border Colorado are the states of Utah, Wyoming, Kansas, Nebraska, Oklahoma, Texas, New Mexico, and Arizona. Failure to name all states correctly does not cost a team penalty points, but it is an indication to other teams that all states named have been correct. If the teacher indicates that no points are to be awarded, that means that the team involved has not named all of the states.

At that point some other team has a chance to step forward, name any remaining states, and gain all eight points for the state of Colorado. For example, if Team A correctly named all of the states that touch Colorado except New Mexico, it would get no points. Nor would it receive any penalty points. The chance would then pass to the next team that calls out "Colorado." If Team B, for example, were to step forward and correctly repeat the names of the other seven states plus add New Mexico, then Team B is awarded all eight points.

If a team names a state that is incorrect, that team is assessed a 5-point penalty. That team's total, therefore, is reduced by five points. The teacher announces the incorrect state and the game passes on to other teams. "Adjacent States" can be played to as many points as desired. Teams will probably have difficulty in getting the names of all the states correct the first few times the game is played.

Place

Place can best be understood by the use of the term *personality*. There are certain characteristics that make a place unique and different from all other places. Place can involve land features (physical characteristics), and it can also mean the sum total of the cultural forms used by the people who live there (human characteristics). This combination of landforms, language spoken, type of homes built, and clothing worn add up to a unique flavor that is not found exactly the same anywhere else. It is these factors that give a place its personality, and that is what the theme of *place* is all about.

TRACKING DOWN TERMS– In presenting this assignment, it is necessary to stress the importance of students learning the meanings of certain geographical terms that will be used throughout their study of the geography of the United States. Asking them to develop their own definitions should help with their understanding, but assigning them the task of pointing to a specific example should reinforce their basic understanding of each concept.

Once students have completed their definitions and examples, entertain a class discussion that allows them to verbalize their definitions and compare them to those of other students. Have them point out on a map of the United States their examples of each geographic term.

An alternative presentation of this lesson involves placing students into small groups to allow them to share the definition/example assignment. An extension of the assignment asks them to create a poster (on 18" x 22" white paper) on which they depict as many of the terms as they can. The only rule is to make the drawing realistic to the point of describing the actual physical geography of the United States. Below are sample definitions of the terms and a single example of each.

bay	Part of a sea or a lake that is partly surrounded by the shore land—San Francisco Bay
canyon	A deep, narrow valley having high, steep sides—Grand Canyon
cape	A narrow part of land along a shore that sticks out into the water—Cape Cod
delta	Land made by the soil that drops from a river at its mouth and places it near where it meets the sea—Mississippi River Delta
desert	Land area in which there is little rainfall and little plant life and growth—Mojave Desert
divide	The highest land that separates two river basins—Continental Divide
gulf	A large area of the sea (or ocean) that lies within a curved coastline—Gulf of Mexico

harbor	A sheltered body of water where ships are safe from high winds—Boston Harbor
island	A body of land completely surrounded by water—Sanibel Island
lake	A body of water surrounded by land—Lake Michigan
mountain	Land that rises much higher than the land at its base—Mt. Whitney
mountain range	A row of mountains that are joined together—Rocky Mountains
peninsula	A land area that is surrounded on all sides by water except for where it is connected to a larger body of land—Florida
plateau	A large land area that is high and generally very flat—Appalachian Plateau
plain	A large body of relatively flat land—Atlantic Coastal Plain
reservoir	A large artificial body of water used to store water for use by irrigation or in the generation of hydroelectric power—Lake Mead
river	A large body of fresh water that starts at a source in higher land and moves to lower land, carrying water to its mouth, where it empties into a larger body of water—Mississippi River
sound	A long and wide body of water connecting two larger bodies of water—Puget Sound
tributary	A stream or smaller river that flows into a larger river—The Illinois River is a tributary of the Mississippi
valley	Low-lying land between hills or mountains—Death Valley

MIGHTY WATERS—This assignment requires reproducing a copy of the outline map of the United States for each student as well as the activity sheet. Use the map that has the boundaries included for each state. Students are asked to chart the paths of some of America's most important rivers. This means there should also be several atlases available for them to use in locating the various rivers. Class discussion should include having students tracing each river on a large wall map, discussing their choices for other rivers they consider important that were not on their list, and identification of the local drinking water source. The extension, which can be used as an optional assignment, involves further research by students on three of the rivers on the list.

MOUNTAIN MAJESTY—This assignment also requires the use of the blank outline map of the United States. Again, use the map that includes the boundary lines of each state. Students locate various important mountain chains contained in the first list. They also locate lesser mountain ranges (of their choice) on the same map. Having several good student atlases on hand is a prerequisite for this assignment! Atlases should be detailed enough to include the less important mountain ranges contained in the second list. The extension involves further research on one of the four categories into which all mountains fall.

CITY FLAVORS—This activity calls for students to identify a single landmark within each of 30 major U.S. cities that help to identify that city and give it a personality that is all its own. Extending this activity could involve students choosing a city and researching other factors that combine to make the city unique from all others.

PACKING FOR PLEASURE—The main objective of this activity is to get students to think about not only the locations of the various "vacation spots," but also to consider the kind of weather conditions that are typical for that particular place during a specific time of year. In addition to clothing choices, students are also asked to identify the kinds of fun activities they would engage in to make each site a memorable experience.

YOUR CHOICE requires both individual thinking on the part of students as well as an entire-class discussion that gives students a chance to share and defend their own personal reasons for their choices. The second page of the activity calls for a group decision on how to portray the information that is collected on the choices of all class members. Allow students to offer their own suggestions on what kind of chart or graph or other presentation could best display the information to someone who knew nothing about the assignment. As an extension activity, students could also follow the same line of thinking in making a choice of countries in which to live. Give them a list of 20–30 countries that includes the United States (or you could exclude it as another option) and ask them to follow the same assignment.

Tracking Down Terms

Understanding the geography of the United States begins with a knowledge of a few terms that will be used from time to time throughout your study. The list below includes 20 such terms. Your task is to find an appropriate definition that will help you to understand the concept of each term. Jot down your definition using words that have meaning to you! Then to prove your understanding of the term, cite an example of

each and pinpoint your example on a map of the United States by neatly labeling its location on the map.

bay - _____

_____

canyon - _____

_____

cape - _____

_____

delta - _____

_____

desert - _____

_____

divide - _____

_____

gulf - _____

_____

harbor - _____

_____

island - _____

_____

lake - _____
_____

mountain - _____
_____

mountain range - _____
_____

peninsula - _____
_____

plateau - _____
_____

plain - _____
_____

reservoir - _____
_____

river - _____
_____

sound - _____
_____

tributary - _____
_____

valley - _____
_____

Mighty Waters

One of the factors that helped our nation historically during its development stages was its internal network of waterways. Rivers served as the main source of transportation and communication during those early days. There is little doubt that the waterways helped to expedite the colonization and settlement of lands west of the Appalachian Mountains. Those same rivers today serve as a cheap method of transporting bulk goods like grain, coal, oil, and other minerals and food products to refineries and finishing plants. Our waterways also serve as a main source of drinking water for many cities. One of our most precious resources, our nation's waterways, have also become major recreation areas for millions of Americans.

Taking a good long look at this wonderful natural resource will help you to understand the importance our waterways have been and continue to be to our entire nation. Your first task is to indicate the path followed by each of the important rivers in the list below. Use a good atlas as your resource and mark each river (complete with labels) on the outline map of the United States provided you for this activity.

Arkansas	Colorado	Columbia
Hudson	Mississippi	Missouri
North Platte	Ohio	Red
Rio Grande	South Platte	Tennessee
White	Yukon	

Look closely at the atlas you used as your source. Name three other rivers you think would be good to include on a list of America's Most Important Rivers.

_____

Rivers often serve as a source of drinking water for cities nearby (and sometimes not so nearby). What is the source of your city's drinking water? _____
If your city does not get its water supply from a river, name some other city that is within your vicinity that does use a river as its water source. _____

Choose three rivers from the list of those you plotted on the outline map and research each, finding out each river's source, its outflow (where it flows into another body of water), and the river's length. Be prepared to share your findings with other members of your class.

Mountain Majesty

The United States has been blessed with a number of mountain ranges that provide us with a wealth of mineral resources. Millions of Americans travel our mountain ranges each year seeking the clean air, the spectacular beauty, and the pleasant summertime temperatures. There are also the hiking, climbing, skiing, camping, and other pleasures associated with a mountain environment. In short, Americans are truly infatuated with these products of the Ice Age.

When asked about where mountains are located in this country, most students readily identify the Rockies with the West and the Appalachians with the East. However, there are several other mountain ranges that should be recognized as well. The purpose of this activity is to spend a few moments learning about the locations of some of these other major mountain ranges.

Using the blank outline map of the United States that has been provided you, pinpoint the locations of the following mountain ranges. You will also need to consult a good atlas that shows the various mountains found in the United States. Use the mountain symbols (∧∧∧) and carefully label each mountain range:

Rocky	Appalachian	Smoky
Sierra Nevada	Cascades	Coast Range
Blue Ridge	Ozark	Green
White	Brooks Range	Aleutian Range

Have you ever visited any of these mountain ranges? If so, reflect back on how you felt the first time you saw them. Describe how they looked at "first view" to you.

_____

_____

_____

_____

There are also several other lesser mountain ranges located in the United States. From the list of 15 below, find the locations of five mountain ranges and indicate their locations on your map:

Ouachitas	Santa Monica	Teton Range
Bighorn Range	Allegheny	Wasatch
Sawtooth	Santa Catalina	Black Hills
Taconic	Pocono	Sangre de Cristo Range
Toiyabe	Clearwater	San Juan

Mountains are classified according to the way in which they were created. Geologists tell us that all mountains fall into one of these five categories: *fold mountains, volcano mountains, dome mountains, fault-block mountains, or erosion mountains.* Research the meanings of these terms. Then choose one mountain range located in the United States that can be identified with one of these classifications. Explain why it falls into that class in the space below and share your findings with other members of your class.

Also indicate the attractions they hold for those who visit them for sport or relaxation.

Name of mountains chosen for research - _____

Classification - _____

Reason(s) for this classification - _____

_____

_____

_____

Attractions for visitors - _____

_____

_____

City Flavors

While most big cities have a lot in common, each has its own identity that makes it unique and different from all other cities. One of the factors that helps to give a city its own identity is a landmark, a symbol, a building, a famous street, a theme park, or a special area within that city that is readily identifiable to others.

For example, when we think of the Statue of Liberty, we immediately think of New York City. Of course there are several other landmarks that we also identify with New York. But there are other cities that have one or two showpieces that give a special identity to those who visit as well as those who live there.

Below is a list of 30 large cities in the United States. Beneath the list is another list of identifiable symbols or landmarks that help to give each city its own special identity. Your task is to match them up.

a. Los Angeles
b. Miami
c. Honolulu
d. San Diego
e. Nashville
f. Phoenix
g. Anaheim
h. Indianapolis
i. Denver
j. Chicago

k. Detroit
l. Washington, D.C.
m. St. Louis
n. Seattle
o. Orlando
p. Philadelphia
q. Louisville
r. Atlanta
s. Houston
t. New Orleans

u. San Francisco
v. San Antonio
w. Boston
x. Salt Lake City
y. Memphis
z. Las Vegas
aa. Dallas
bb. Baltimore
cc. New York City
dd. Tampa

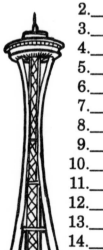

1._____Sears Tower
2._____Epcot Center
3._____The Alamo
4._____Liberty Bell
5._____Mile High Stadium
6._____Space Needle
7._____Motor Speedway
8._____Bourbon Street
9._____USS *Arizona*
10._____1996 Olympic Games
11._____Balboa Park
12._____Camelback
13._____Grand Ole Opry
14._____Beale Street
15._____The Cowboys

16._____Caesar's Palace
17._____Empire State Building
18._____General Motors
19._____Golden Gate Bridge
20._____Disneyland
21._____Gateway Arch
22._____Beacon Hill
23._____The White House
24._____Orange Bowl
25._____NASA
26._____Rodeo Drive
27._____Ft. McHenry
28._____Busch Gardens
29._____Churchill Downs
30._____Mormon Tabernacle

Packing for Pleasure

Americans go on vacation for a variety of reasons, but the big reason is *always* to have fun! They also go to a variety of places and they go under varying weather conditions. Some seek the sunshine of a crowded beach. Others consider the beauty of nature when making their vacation choice. Some go for the sport of it all (golf, tennis, skiing), while others are on historical or "landmark" missions. And then there are those who just want to "get away from it all."

But regardless of *where* they go or *when* they go, they all want to feel comfortable. To do this requires a lot of thinking ahead of time to make certain just the right clothing and "extras" are packed for the trip.

The vacation spots below offer a wide variety of places and seasons for the American tourist. Look carefully at each scenario. Then do a bit of research to find out just what kind of weather is "typical" for that particular location at that time of year. You can find such information in any good travel guide. Be certain to consider the low temperatures as well as the highs and the other weather conditions that prevail. In the space that follows each plan, jot down the type of clothing you would choose to take. Include any other "essentials" that would be important to make such an experience a great vacation for you. You should also include a short explanation of what your plans would be once you were to get to such vacation "hot spots."

Waikiki Beach on the island of Oahu in mid-January

_____

_____

_____

_____

Branson, Missouri, in mid-July

_____

_____

_____

_____

Estes Park, Colorado, during the second week in March

_____

_____

_____

_____

San Diego, California, during the first week in September

_____

_____

The Grand Canyon during the second week in July

_____

_____

Disney World during Thanksgiving vacation

_____

_____

A tour of Washington, D.C., and nearby Williamsburg during the first week in June

_____

_____

Hilton Head Island during the second week in April

_____

_____

Vermont, New Hampshire, and Maine in September

_____

_____

Chicago in August

_____

_____

New Orleans during Mardi Gras

_____

_____

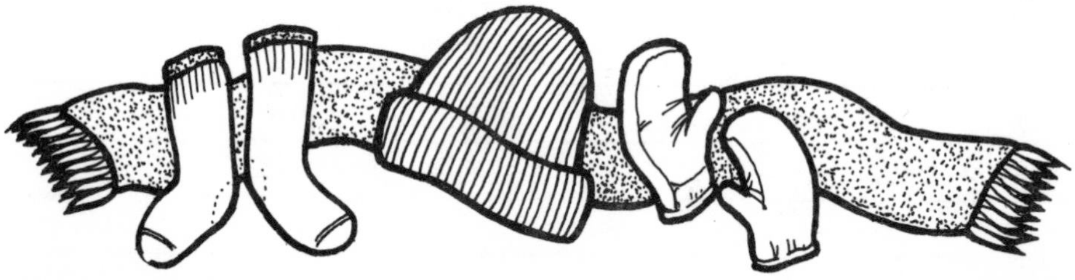

Touring the Back Roads

The United States certainly has been blessed with more than its share of historic landmarks. If you study the history behind these famous places, you will soon see how each makes its own individual contribution in telling the true story of America. That is the big story—and certainly millions of Americans center their vacations around making annual pilgrimages to some of these landmarks just to be there and feel that touch with our heritage and past history.

But in reality, these famous places tell only part of the story. There are literally hundreds of less famous places that lay claim to a stake in the American story as well. After all, what would a study of America be without a first-hand, true-to-life experience in Hershey's Chocolate World in Hershey, Pennsylvania, or a look at the world's largest peanut in Pearsall, Texas?

Charles Karault, the long-time travel guru of CBS television, spent much of his professional career touring the "Back Roads of America." He shared his discoveries on a weekly basis and Americans loved him for it!

On the next page are just a few of these "back road treasures" that many people often overlook. Some are so obscure and insignificant that they are missed for obvious reasons; others are really worthwhile experiences. But because they do not get enough advertising hype, people simply do not know about them. Read the description of each of the examples; then pinpoint its location on the blank map of the United States.

To find the location of each, you will need to look at a state or local map that will give you a good idea of the exact location of the landmark. Identify each attraction's location by placing a dot on the blank outline map. Then neatly print the name of the attraction next to the dot. In the blank space following the description of each location, indicate directions on how you would go about getting there from where you currently live. You obviously would not center your vacation around travelling to one of these roadside gems, but this activity is an exercise in pinpointing the locations of places with real personalities all their own. So part of the fun is in describing how to get there.

WALL DRUG in Wall, South Dakota, is visited by over one million people every year! Its location was billed as "in the middle of nowhere" with highway wooden road signs all over America announcing to tourists exactly the number of miles from that point to Wall Drug. It started as a place for free ice water years ago. Today it has grown into a multi-million dollar business that many tourists consider a must when they are close by. Many of those wooden road signs are gone today, but Wall Drug lives on, enjoying a clientele from all over the world. Many come just to say that they have been there! There's a lot more to Wall Drug than just a drug store!

How to get there from where I live

_____

_____

_____

TOMBSTONE, ARIZONA, "The Town Too Tough to Die," is perhaps the most famous wild West town of them all. When Ed Schieffelin came to Cam Huachuca with a party of soldiers and left the fort to prospect, his comrades told him that he would find his tombstone rather than silver. Schieffelin named his first claim Tombstone, and rumors spread about how rich silver strikes turned the place into a boomtown. As was the case in many of those early western boomtowns, lawlessness and violence prevailed. Tombstone's most famous moment came during the infamous Earp-Clanton battle fought near the entrance to the O.K. Corral. The famous gun battle is reenacted on a daily basis, drawing thousands of tourists every year.

How to get there from where I live

_____

_____

_____

GRACELAND MANSION in Memphis, Tennessee, is the site of the most ambitious of tributes to rock star Elvis Presley. Over a half million fans of Presley visit this shrine annually. The famous mansion, which became Elvis' home, includes Meditation Gardens, where he is buried. The memorabilia and furnishings (including shag carpet on the ceilings, leopard skins, and the three TVs where Elvis watched the nightly news) of the mansion make it a "must-see" for Elvis fans.

How to get there from where I live

_____

_____

_____

THE FIRST MCDONALD'S, where fast-food franchises began, is located in Des Plaines, Illinois. The small building is the scene where Ray Kroc began building his fast-food empire beneath the golden arches in 1955. Burger lovers can enjoy all the memorabilia associated with the franchise—then satisfy their fast-food desires in a new McDonald's conveniently located nearby. Tourists should be forewarned that burgers are no longer 15 cents!

How to get there from where I live

_____

_____

_____

RICHARD NIXON LIBRARY AND BIRTHPLACE in Yorba Linda, California, is also the grave site of the former president. In 1994 Nixon was buried just a few feet from where he was born. Visitors can follow "The Road to the Presidency" as they view various memorabilia associated with the Nixon Years.

How to get there from where I live

_____

_____

_____

STONE MOUNTAIN, near Atlanta, Georgia, features the world's largest bas relief sculpture, a tribute to Confederate leaders Robert E. Lee, Stonewall Jackson, and Jefferson Davis. The 3,200-acre park also features other historical and recreational facilities, including an antebellum plantation, riverboat cruises, and a lakefront beach.

How to get there from where I live

_____

_____

_____

FOLLOW THE YELLOW BRICK ROAD as well as visit a replica of Dorothy's house from the Land of Oz in Liberal, Kansas. Visitors embark on an animated sight and sound journey through Oz (including a pair of supposedly genuine ruby slippers and an Oz minimuseum) and enjoy a wide variety of area and western exhibits to add to the attraction.

How to get there from where I live

_____

_____

_____

INDIANAPOLIS MOTOR SPEEDWAY is where auto racing fans can board a bus and actually experience the thrill of a trip around the famed 2½ mile oval, site of the annual Memorial Day Indy 500. The race is billed as the "Biggest Spectacle in Sports," attracting literally hundreds of thousands of race fans. The accompanying race museum adds to the visit, but fans must accept the 35 miles-per-hour speed of the bus rather than the 200+ miles-per-hour ride the car drivers experience during the race.

How to get there from where I live

_____

_____

_____

Now it is your turn! Through travel brochures, historical maps, travel guides, atlases, or whatever other resources you choose to use, your final assignment in this activity is to point to some of those "roadside gems" of your own choosing. Pick two places of interest to you. Point out why you think they are worthy of mention. Then locate them on your map and create a simple set of instructions to others on how to get to each from where you currently live.

CHOICE #1

_____

_____

_____

_____

CHOICE #2

_____

_____

_____

_____

Your Choice

Perhaps you have thought about how great it would be if you could live somewhere else. It goes with the "grass is always greener" feeling that a lot of people have. Or maybe you are one of those who think you are living in THE best place right now! Either way, you are going to have a chance to express your choice.

There are 50 great states in this country, and every one of them has a number of reasons why people have chosen to live there. If we stop for a moment and ask ourselves why people live where they live, we come up with a list that includes factors like job opportunity, relatives nearby, desirable climate, scenic beauty, cultural attractions, physical geography, exciting things to do, quality of life—and the list goes on.

Think about your own situation. Why is your family currently living where you live? What is the history behind your current location?

Even though job opportunity is often the most important factor for a family being where it is, we are going to assume for this assignment that you have complete freedom of choice. After you have given the matter some thought, record your choices in the grid on the next page. There is a space for your top choice—that state where you would rather live than any other. Then there are four other boxes where you should record your second, third, fourth, and fifth choices.

When you begin to think about where you want to live, there will no doubt be thoughts that pass through your mind on places where you definitely would NOT want to live. The second row of boxes is for use in recording those choices. In the first box you should record the name of the state that ranks lowest on your list of priorities. The next four boxes should be filled with other names of states where you would prefer not to live. The second box would be your next to least favorite choice (i.e., #49). Continue the same pattern for the remaining three boxes.

© Frank Schaffer Publications, Inc. FS-10181 Geography . . . USA

	Top Choice	#2	#3	#4	#5
Where I would like to live:					

	Top Choice	#2	#3	#4	#5
Where I would not want to live:					

1. Make a list of the reasons for the choices you made as your preferences. Are there similar reasons for your first five choices, or were those five choices made for a variety of reasons? Place your list in the space below and make any comments that account for the similarities or differences of reasons for choice.

_____

_____

_____

_____

2. Follow the same kind of thinking in deciding the reasons for your least favorite states in which you would want to live. Were these "least favorite" choices made on the basis of direct information you know about the states, or were they made because of the comments made by others? Were you in any way influenced by your own personal firsthand knowledge of these places? Describe your reasoning in the space below.

_____

_____

_____

_____

3. Share your thoughts with other members of your class. As you listen to the comments and choices made by others (on both their top choices and their least favorite choices), can you think of any way you might combine all this information into some kind of conclusion that sums up the feelings of your class? Record your thoughts below. Then participate in a class discussion in which your class actually develops a chart or graph or some other way of presenting the choices of the entire class.

_____

_____

_____

_____

Movement

Movement is the theme of geography that investigates the dependence of people on one another. It includes the study of movement patterns in communication, transportation, and in the people themselves. Movement also involves studying the transport of goods and services from their source to the ultimate consumer. Finally, there is a concern about distances of places from one another. Through the activities found in this unit, students should begin to see some of those patterns through the generalizations and conclusions they draw from the assignments they complete.

IN THE CENTER OF EVERYWHERE—This assignment will help students to see visually how the population of the United States has shifted. Its historical beginning in the East followed by the westward expansion are only part of the story. Discuss with students the other factors that have contributed to the continued shift of the population center.

REPRESENTATION IN CONGRESS—Students analyze the shift in population by comparing statistics from the 1900 and 1990 censuses. Before assigning this activity, entertain a discussion on the historical implications of the "equal representation" philosophy that was championed by the smaller states during the drafting stages of the Constitution. Investigate the battle between the small and large states over the matter of representation that was eventually solved by the establishment of a bicameral lawmaking body.

THE 25 LARGEST U.S. CITIES—Students compare the population growth of our nation's largest cities, using 1980 and 1990 census figures. The assignment involves a statistical analysis, but it will also lead them to some conclusions about the cities that are growing the most and the locations of those cities. This lesson is best presented by dividing students into pairs to allow them to share some of the math responsibilities. Students should also have access to calculators for this assignment.

WE LIVE IN A SHRINKING WORLD—This activity emphasizes our dependence on one another for the fulfillment of the many goods and services that make our lives more convenient and comfortable than they would be if we had to fend for ourselves. To get those goods and services to people in their homes, their jobs, and the places they use for recreation and relaxation requires a whole lot of movement! Students are given 12 examples of products (or raw materials) and asked to trace the kind of movement that would most probably be used in transporting that product from one place to another.

CONNECTING FLIGHTS—This activity involves students investigating the abbreviations used for identifying several major airports throughout the United States. Attempting to guess the city with the abbreviation will allow them a high degree of success, but some of the abbreviations offer virtually no clue about the cities in which they are located. Providing students with flight directories from major airlines will allow them to check their answers and bring up other interesting letter combinations for further investigation. An extension of this assignment involves students actually launching an investigation into the reason(s) for some of the less identifiable letter abbreviations.

DO YOU HAVE THE TIME?—Distribute a copy of the time zones map of the United States to each student for use with both this activity and the next ("Changing Times"). Explain the mathematical reasoning for each time zone containing 15° of longitude. Discuss with students reasons for the various time zones not following perfectly straight lines. Be certain to include the "airline challenge" if time permits. Students enjoy creating travel scenarios to challenge others. The challenge to them is to make the problems realistic; the value in the assignment is to develop a sense of how long it takes to get from one place to another (by air) in various parts of the United States.

CHANGING TIMES—Use the map on time zones for answering the questions in this activity. Be certain students understand how to add or subtract hours in moving from one time zone to another. Go over a few of the initial questions together before assigning students the rest of the activity to be completed on their own.

THE MAIN VEINS OF AMERICA—It is important for students to have access to an accurate atlas showing the entire interstate highway system within the United States. A good way to introduce the activity is to inquire into student knowledge of area interstate highways. How do they differ from other highways? How are they numbered? This assignment lends itself well to students either working with a partner or alone. When it comes time to share answers, make a transparency of the map and place it on an overhead projector so all students can see where any mistakes may have been made. The transparency can also be used if it is the teacher's desire to make the activity an entire-class assignment.

CROSSING AMERICA—This assignment takes students on a map reading of a west coast-to-east coast journey from Los Angeles to Miami. Since each new stop along the way is dependent upon getting the prior city stop correct, it is important that students have access to an accurate atlas. It would also be good to have all students do the assignment at the same time. This can be accomplished at school (if enough atlases are available), or it can be used as a take-home assignment. Once you have gone over the correct answers, it is time to turn around and go the other way. This time the east coast-to-west coast trip starts in Philadelphia and takes students to an eventual destination of San Francisco. When both assignments are complete, have students create their own version to be exchanged with a friend. Partners then work on each other's choices and check their accuracy when finished.

In the Center of Everywhere

The *center of population* is that point in the United States where there are just as many people living north as there are south and just as many people living to the east as there are to the west. This point is recalculated and plotted at the end of each census. Can you think of any reasons why demographers concern themselves with such trivia?

Below are the described locations of some of those points in America that have served as the population center following the censuses taken in the indicated years. Look at a good political map (or state maps if necessary) to find the relative locations of these points; then plot them on the map below by placing a dot on the location and then identifying the dot with the year of the census. For example, the population center following the 1790 census is already plotted for you.

1790   23 miles east of Baltimore, Maryland
1810   40 miles northwest of Washington, D.C.
1840   16 miles south of Clarksburg, West Virginia
1870   48 miles northeast of Cincinnati, Ohio
1900   6 miles southeast of Columbus, Indiana
1930   3 miles northeast of Linton, Indiana
1960   6 miles northwest of Centralia, Illinois
1980   De Soto, Missouri
1990   9 miles northwest of Steelville, Missouri

Once you have located the population centers, connect them with a single line. What conclusions can you draw about the shift of population within the United States during the past 200 years?

_____

_____

Where do you think the population center might be 100 years from now (in the year 2090)? Of course it is anybody's guess, but for what reasons did you mark the choice you made?

_____

_____

Below are the *geographical extremities* of the United States. Find these locations on a good political map of the United States and plot in their locations on the map on the previous page.

North - Point Barrow, Alaska   South - South Cape, Hawaii

East - West Quoddy Head, Maine   West - Cape Wrangell, Alaska

The two places in the United States that are separated by the greatest distance are Kure Island, Hawaii, and Log Point, Elliot Key, Florida, a distance of almost 6,000 miles apart!

The *geographic center* of the United States (including Alaska and Hawaii is in Butte County, South Dakota, at 44° North Latitude, 103° West Longitude. Plot this approximate location on your map.

In which direction is the current *population center* from the *geographic center*?

_____

Which border is longer, the boundary between the United States and Canada or the boundary between the United States and Mexico?_____

Which U.S. coastline is longer, the Atlantic or the Pacific?_____

Representation in Congress

The accompanying map shows the various regions of the United States as identified by the U.S. Bureau of the Census. The number within the boundaries of each state is the number of members that state elects to the U.S. House of Representatives. According to provisions outlined in the original U.S. Constitution, the number of representatives to which each state is entitled would be based on the most recent population. The figures represented on the map are based on the 1990 Census.

Analyze carefully the information contained in the map and answer the questions below.

1. Which state has the largest number of representatives in Congress?

   _____

2. Name in descending order the next four states that have the largest representation in the House of Representatives. Include the number after each state.

   2. _____ 3. _____ 4. _____

   5. _____

3. Which states have the smallest populations (and thus only one representative)? Use abbreviations: _____

   _____

4. What is the total number of members in the U.S. House of Representatives?

   _____

5. Which of the four regions has the greatest number of representatives?

   _____

   Which has the fewest?_____

6. Which of the regions has the greatest number of states? _____
   Which has the smallest number of states? _____

7. The U.S. Bureau of the Census lists the 1990 official population of the United States at 248,709,873. If there is truly "equal representation" in Congress, what would be the ideal number of people represented by each congressman?

   _____

8. What is the name of your U.S. congressman?_____

9. How many members of the U.S. House of Representatives are from your state?_____ Find out how many representatives your state had during the 1980s._____ Has the number changed?_____

10. What do these two numbers tell you about the population of your state? Is your state gaining in population, losing people, or did the population remain relatively the same?_____

The first official U.S. census was taken in the year 1790. The results showed a country with fewer than 4 million people. The entire concentration of that population was in the New England states and other states along the east coast. By the time the census in 1800 was taken, the population had grown to approximately 5.3 million people and included people who had started moving into more western territories.

By the year 1900 the pioneer movement had spread people all over the United States. Below are some statistics that show the percentage of total population each of the four major geographical regions claimed.

	1900 Census	1990 Census
Northeast	27.5	20.5
South	32.3	34.3
Midwest	34.4	24.1
West	5.8	21.1

11. Based on these statistics from the Bureau of the Census, what two major shifts in population have occurred during the past 90 years?

   _____

12. Based on these percentages, how many of the 435 representatives should each area have?
   Calculate each and record in the spaces below:

   Northeast_____ South_____Midwest_____West_____

13. How do these numbers compare with the actual apportionment that was determined after the 1990 census? Add the totals from the states in each area and record the results below:

   Northeast_____South_____Midwest_____West_____

United States Congressional Representation

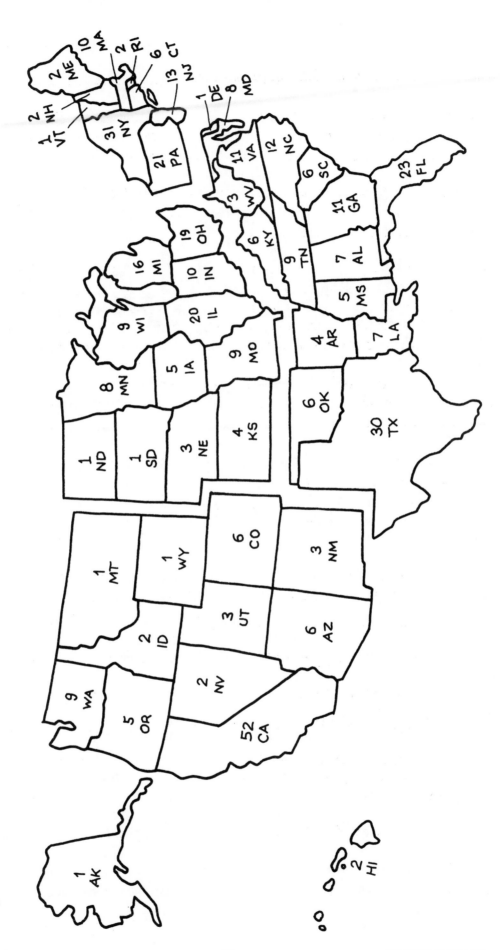

The 25 Largest U.S. Cities

On the following page are recent population figures for the 25 largest cities in the United States. The first column indicates the population according to the 1990 Census. The second column has the 1980 official U.S. Census figures. The numbers include only people actually living within the city limits of the cities indicated. They do not include the outlying metropolitan areas.

Your task in this activity is to analyze the data from the two censuses provided. To help speed up the process, you will need both a friend and a calculator. Your partner will need a calculator, too. Teaming up with a classmate will help you to overcome possible "calculator fatigue," will prevent severe eye strain, and will allow you to divide the calculations and thus move on to the analysis stage (which is what you are after in the first place) more quickly.

The third column asks you to calculate the net gain (or loss) in total population for each city during this 10-year period between the 1980 and 1990 censuses. The fourth column then asks you to calculate the percentage gain (or loss) during the decade of the eighties. Round your calculations off to the nearest tenth of a percent.

The presentation of cities is in descending order of their current size according to the 1990 census. For example, New York City had a population of 7,322,564 people. In 1980 it had 7,071,639. The net gain was thus 250,925, which represented a rise of 3.6 percent (to the nearest tenth of a percent). Remember to divide the labor of calculating these numbers with a partner. It might also be a good idea to check each result just to make certain you are correct.

Name _____

Name of City	1990 Population	1980 Population	Net Gain	Percentage
1. New York	7,322,564	7,071,639	250,925	3.5%
2. Los Angeles	3,485,398	2,966,850	_____	_____
3. Chicago	2,783,726	3,005,072	_____	_____
4. Houston	1,630,553	1,595,138	_____	_____
5. Philadelphia	1,585,577	1,688,210	_____	_____
6. San Diego	1,110,549	875,538	_____	_____
7. Detroit	1,027,974	1,203,368	_____	_____
8. Dallas	1,007,618	904,078	_____	_____
9. Phoenix	983,395	789,704	_____	_____
10. San Antonio	935,933	785,880	_____	_____
11. San Jose	782,952	629,442	_____	_____
12. Indianapolis	741,952	700,807	_____	_____
13. Baltimore	736,014	786,741	_____	_____
14. San Francisco	723,959	678,974	_____	_____
15. Jacksonville	672,971	540,920	_____	_____
16. Columbus	632,945	564,871	_____	_____
17. Milwaukee	628,088	636,212	_____	_____
18. Memphis	610,337	646,170	_____	_____
19. Washington, D.C.	606,900	638,432	_____	_____
20. Boston	574,283	562,994	_____	_____
21. Seattle	516,259	493,846	_____	_____
22. El Pasos	515,342	425,259	_____	_____
23. Nashville	510,784	455,651	_____	_____
24. Cleveland	505,616	573,822	_____	_____
25. New Orleans	496,938	557,927	_____	_____

Now that you have done all the calculations, team up with your partner to analyze your data and answer the questions below:

1. How many of these major U.S. cities gained in population? _____

2. How many actually lost in population between the 1980 census and the 1990 census? _____

3. Which city remained closest to showing no change in population? _____

4. How many cities showed a net gain in population of at least 10 percent? _____

5. Which city showed the greatest net gain in the number of people living there?

_____

6. Which city showed the greatest percentage of gain in population? _____

7. Which city had the greatest exodus (net loss of population) during the 1980s?

_____

8. Which city showed the greatest percentage of loss in population during the1980s?

_____

9. Name the ten cities that showed the greatest percentage gains in population during the 1980s. Your list should be in descending order with the top city first. Also include the percentage gain of each of these cities.

1. _____ _____   6. _____ _____
2. _____ _____   7. _____ _____
3. _____ _____   8. _____ _____
4. _____ _____   9. _____ _____
5. _____ _____   10. _____ _____

10. Are there any conclusions you can draw about those cities that showed the greatest increase in population? Look closely at your list and jot down any conclusions you and your partner reach in the space below.

_____

_____

_____

11. Which five cities showed the greatest percentage of net loss during this decade? List them in descending order and include their percentage loss in your list.

1. _____ _____
2. _____ _____
3. _____ _____
4. _____ _____
5. _____ _____

12. Can you think of any reasons why these cities might have lost so many people? Place the theories of you and your partner in the space below that might explain specific loss of population in these five cities. Then list reasons in general why people move out of cities.

_____

_____

_____

13. OPTIONAL ASSIGNMENT: For purposes of comparison, figure out from the numbers on page 53 the rank order of big city population following the 1980 census. You will need to know that Denver had a population of 492,694 in 1980 and St. Louis had 452,801 people. Population figures for those cities are not shown on the first page of this activity because they were not among the nation's 25 largest cities in 1990. Place your list of the top 25 U.S. cities (according to the 1980 census) in the space below.

1. _____   13. _____
2. _____   14. _____
3. _____   15. _____
4. _____   16. _____
5. _____   17. _____
6. _____   18. _____
7. _____   19. _____
8. _____   20. _____
9. _____   21. _____
10. _____   22. _____
11. _____   23. _____
12. _____   24. _____
                                       25. _____

Compare this list with the list following the 1990 census.

_____

_____

_____

_____

_____

We Live in a Shrinking World

You have no doubt heard that statement before. Just what does it mean? For one thing, it means that we really are not very self-sufficient any more. We live in a very comfortable and convenient world; and to make it all happen that way, we have come to depend on others to provide us with the goods and services that satisfy our needs. It would probably be very difficult for any of us to perform for even a short period of time as the pioneers and early explorers did in satisfying their needs as the occasion arose.

Much of this dependence is really good, because it makes our lives much more convenient and comfortable than they would be if we had to fend for ourselves at every step of the way. It also provides an opportunity for most adults to work as they find their own personal niche in helping to satisfy the needs or desires of others by specializing in one particular job or line of work. In exchange for helping to provide for the needs of others, they are paid money which they can in turn use to buy the goods and services needed and desired by their families. Think about the current work of your own parents. Do they do work that can be related to performing some kind of work for the convenience or comfort of others?

All of this dependence upon others causes a great deal of movement of goods and services that come from a wide variety of sources and places. Some of those places are close by, in fact, within the same cities or towns where we live. Others come from a distance of thousands of miles.

Below are a few examples of products (or services) that become a part of our lives because they are moved to us from another place. After reading each situation, decide the method you think is most likely used to make that product or service of use to you. Some will have more than one possibility. List your preference, but think of any other possibilities.

Oil taken from the oil fields of northern Alaska to the port of Valdez

_____

_____

Automobiles from the assembly line in Detroit, Michigan, to a dealership in Charleston, South Carolina

_____

_____

The biweekly commission paycheck of a traveling salesman living in Illinois who works for a company based in Los Angeles, California

_____

_____

Corn picked from fields in Iowa that will be processed into food for cattle and hogs at a factory located in Chicago, Illinois

_____

_____

A baseball game televised live from Yankee Stadium in New York City to a home in Salt Lake City, Utah

_____

_____

Water from the Colorado River to resident homes in Phoenix, Arizona

_____

_____

A request by a University of Arkansas senior to his dad in Tacoma, Washington, for more spending money for the current month

_____

_____

The visual okay of a cartoon illustration done by a free lance artist living in Boston who has created the illustration for a newspaper in Miami, Florida

_____

_____

Live Maine lobster caught off the coast at Cape Cod and delivered to a famous restaurant in Cincinnati, Ohio, that advertises "Fresh Catch Daily"

_____

_____

Grain sent from Quincy, Illinois, to a processing plant in New Orleans, Louisiana

_____

_____

Toys sent from the warehouse of a parent company in Cleveland, Ohio, to one of the company's department stores in Philadelphia, Pennsylvania

_____

_____

Fresh oranges and lemons from the citrus groves of Florida to a retail grocery chain based in Nashville, Tennessee

_____

_____

Now, go back through your answers. Were there other possibilities? Were there situations in which there was possibly more than one mode of movement involved in the transfer of the product or service from its point of destination to the eventual consumer? Share your choices with other members of your class.

Then in the remaining space below, compose a list of several products or services that are a part of your life that come from other places. After describing each, define the kind of movement you think has brought that product (or service) to you.

_____

_____

_____

_____

_____

_____

_____

_____

_____

_____

_____

_____

_____

_____

Connecting Flights

Each airport in the United States has three letters of identification that serve as its official abbreviation. Those letters often show a strong hint of the city's location. For example, the letters DEN are the letters used to indicate the airport in Denver. The airport in San Diego is abbreviated with the use of the letters SAN. However, some of the letters used are not so obvious in identifying with the city in which the airport is located. For example, the letters ORD are used to indicate O'Hare International in Chicago.

Below are several sets of letters used to stand for other major airports in the United States. Use your imagination to see if you can figure out what city the letters stand for in each case. Some of them you may not be able to guess, but you will have fun trying anyway. When you are finished, exchange your list with a friend, verify your answers, and correct any mistakes.

1. _____ DEN
2. _____ BOS
3. _____ LAS
4. _____ DFW
5. _____ PHL
6. _____ SEA
7. _____ LAX
8. _____ STL
9. _____ TPA
10. _____ PHX

11. _____ ATL
12. _____ ABQ
13. _____ JFK
14. _____ IND
15. _____ BWI
16. _____ MSP
17. _____ MCI
18. _____ DTW
19. _____ SLC
20. _____ RNO

21. _____ PDX
22. _____ SDF
23. _____ TUS
24. _____ MKE
25. _____ LGA
26. _____ IAH
27. _____ OMA
28. _____ OAK
29. _____ DCA
30. _____ MCO

Do You Have the Time?

While the earth is certainly not a "perfect world," neither is it a perfect sphere, either! However it does come close to being a sphere, so it is said to contain 360°. We all know that it takes 24 hours for the earth to spin on its own axis one time. If we divide the 360° by those 24 hours, it stands to reason that there are 15° of longitude in each time zone.

That is just about the way it really is, except for the fact that time zones do not follow perfectly the medians of longitude. Life is confusing enough as it is! Crossing from one time zone to another sometimes confuses people even more. Thus, for the convenience of people, time zones follow along entire-state boundary lines.

When traveling by air, changing times zones simply becomes a part of life. The TV shows people watch, the business contacts they make on a daily basis, and the contacts with friends and relatives in other parts of the United States all justify a good understanding of time zones.

Look at the map that accompanies this activity to answer the following questions:

1. How many hours separate the clocks of New York City from those in Los Angeles?
   _____

2. If it is 4:00 p.m. in Los Angeles, and you are on a plane bound for New York, what time should you set your watch for when the plane takes off?_____

3. In traveling by air, should you *advance* or *set back* your watch if you are traveling in an east-to-west direction?_____

4. If you want to watch a football game that is scheduled for a 9:00 p.m. EST kickoff, and you live in Springfield, Illinois, at what time should you tune in?_____

5. What are the names of the four time zones found in the Continental United States?_____   _____   _____   _____

6. If a plane leaves Phoenix, Arizona, at 10:45 a.m. bound for St. Louis, Missouri, at what time will it arrive in St. Louis (local time) if the flight lasts two hours and 50 minutes?_____

7. Albert wants to call his mother (who lives in Albuquerque), but he does not want to wake her up. His mother *never* gets up before 7:00 a.m. Albert lives in Baltimore. So what time do you suggest as the earliest time he can field his "wake-up" call to his mother to wish her a happy birthday?_____

8. If the U.S. Open telecast from just outside San Francisco comes on the air at 2:30 p.m. PDT, what time should someone in Miami prepare to watch the tournament?_____

9. A plane leaves New York City at 8:30 a.m. It arrives at its destination on time in Kansas City 2 hours and 8 minutes later. What time was the plane's scheduled arrival in Kansas City?_____

10. A plane leaves San Francisco at 6:50 a.m. bound for Chicago. It has one stop in Las Vegas and arrives at O'Hare on time at 2:35 p.m. How long (in hours and minutes) did the trip actually take including the stop in Las Vegas?_____

11. A plane leaves Philadelphia at 9:50 p.m. bound for San Diego. The plane has one scheduled stop in Columbus, where it will be on the ground for 1 hour and 20 minutes. If the total time in which the plane is in the air (or awaiting takeoff or landing) is 5 hours and 20 minutes, what time will the plane land in San Diego if it is on time?_____

12. If a plane that leaves New York's La Guardia Airport at 9:15 a.m., has a one-hour layover in Las Vegas, and is scheduled to arrive in Salt Lake City on a trip that should take 7 hours and 29 minutes altogether, at what time will the plane arrive in Salt Lake City if it is 23 minutes late?_____

In the space below, make up a similar "airline challenge" to try to stump one of your fellow classmates. Either consult a flight schedule timetable to get some actual times— or better yet, figure out your own. Be certain to make the problem realistic by closely examining the time zones you plan to use. Work the problem yourself first so you will have the correct answer; then exchange your problem with a friend and work each other's problems.

_____

_____

_____

_____

_____

_____

_____

_____

_____

_____

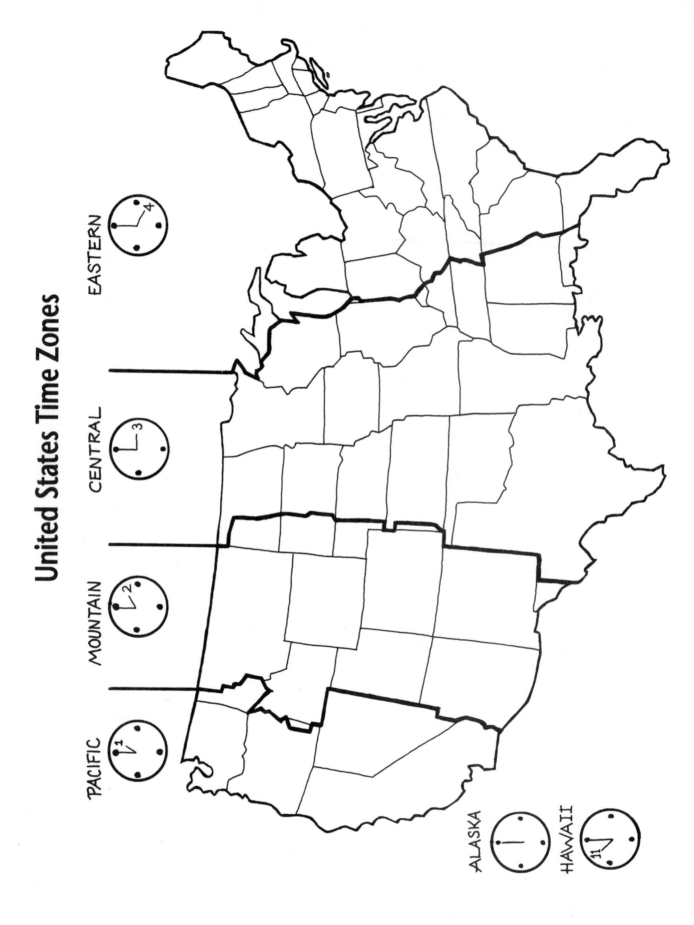

United States Time Zones

EASTERN

CENTRAL

MOUNTAIN

PACIFIC

ALASKA

HAWAII

© Frank Schaffer Publications, Inc.

FS-10181 Geography . . . USA

Name _____

Changing Times

Look at the map that accompanies this activity to answer the following questions that compare your time zone to others.

What time is it where you live . . .

1. if it is 8:45 a.m. in Los Angeles, California?_____

2. if it is 8:15 p.m. in New Orleans, Louisiana?_____

3. if it is 4:45 a.m. in Philadelphia, Pennsylvania?_____

4. if it is 7:20 p.m. in Albuquerque, New Mexico?_____

5. if it is 8:00 a.m. in Atlanta, Georgia?_____

6. if it is 4:00 a.m. in Honolulu, Hawaii?_____

7. if it is 3:40 a.m. in San Diego, California?_____

8. if it is 10:52 a.m. in Phoenix, Arizona?_____

9. if it is 9:55 p.m. in Anchorage, Alaska?_____

10. if it is 4:00 a.m. in Grand Tetons National Park?_____

11. if it is 5:42 a.m. in Williamsburg, Virginia?_____

12. if it is 11:30 p.m. in the Grand Canyon?_____

13. if it is 5:00 p.m. on the Golden Gate Bridge?_____

14. if it is 2:33 p.m. on Mt. Rushmore?_____

15. if it is 3:30 a.m. in our nation's Capitol?_____

16. if it is 3:30 p.m. on Sanibel Island?_____

17. if it is 7:59 a.m. at Epcot Center?_____

18. if it is 4:00 p.m. in the "Mile High City"?_____

19. if it is 5:00 p.m. in Smoky Mountain National Park?_____

20. if it is 3:15 p.m. in Coronado National Forest?_____

Name _____

The Main Veins of America

Since the days when the first highways were built along the paths blazed by earlier cattle trails, the highway has remained the most important method of transportation in the United States. As the population continued to grow, the two-lane highways became inadequate to accommodate the increased flood of traffic.

The result was the National Interstate System. Built to facilitate a faster and more efficient movement of people and products, the interstate system included wider roads that had a minimum of at least two lanes of traffic going in either direction. Slower traffic could stay in the right lane, while the faster traffic could pass and move more quickly in the left lane. There were also entrance and exit ramps and interchanges that connected with other freeways to keep the traffic continually on the move. As long as everything flows smoothly, traffic *never stops* on the freeways.

Thousands of miles of freeways have combined to link all of the major metropolitan areas of the United States. If you look at a good map that shows the U.S. Interstate System, you can probably imagine similarities between the arteries that run throughout the body and these "concrete arteries" that literally "connect" various parts of America.

Use a good road atlas to answer the questions below and on the next page. Read each question carefully; then seek out the appropriate answer on the map. Record your answer in the blank space provided.

1. Do you see more interstate highways *east* or *west* of the Mississippi River?
   _____

2. Which state appears to have the most freeway miles? _____

3. Do more interstate highways run *north and south* or *east and west*?
   _____ What possible explanation can you offer for your answer?

   _____

4. Look at the numbers on several of the interstate highways. What general statements can you make about the way in which the freeways are numbered?

   _____

5. Which east/west highway passes through Jackson, Mississippi?_____

6. Which north/south highway passes through Denver?_____

7. Which north/south highway passes through Minneapolis?_____

8. Which north/south interstate passes through the city of Atlanta?_____

9. What are the end-point cities for I-10? _____

10. What is Nashville's link to Mobile, Alabama?_____

11. How is Philadelphia connected to Pittsburgh?_____

12. Which city marks the western end-of-the-line for I-80?_____

13. Which east/west interstate highway ends at San Diego?_____

14. How does Indianapolis connect to Cincinnati?_____

15. What is I-55's northernmost city?_____

16. What are the end-point cities for I-55?_____

17. What is Portland's connection to Seattle?_____

18. Which freeway connects Louisville to St. Louis?_____

19. Where does I-70 intersect with I-71?_____

20. Where does I-40 cross I-25?_____

21. At what city does I-94 cross I-75?_____

22. What interstate highway connects Cleveland to Buffalo?_____

23. Indianapolis is referred to as "Circle City" because of all the freeways that intersect there. Name all the interstates that "come together" at Indianapolis.

_____

24. Which freeway leads into Las Vegas?_____

25. The Upper Peninsula in Michigan is served by this north/south freeway all the way to the Canadian border._____

26. This single freeway would be used by someone traveling from Rapid City, South Dakota, to Seattle._____

27. The Chicago/St. Louis "connection" is called _____.

28. Which interstate follows the east coast all the way south to Florida?_____

29. In traveling from Charlotte to New Orleans, which freeways do you suggest?_____

30. The freeway that connects the cities of the west coast of the United States is

_____.

Crossing America

Millions of Americans travel across the United States every day. Their journey which took the pioneers months to make can be made in a matter of a few short hours if they travel by air today. Of course travel by car takes longer, but it is still a matter of days rather than months. For this activity you will be using a combination of mental estimation of distances between cities and a road map that shows the interstates that connect America. A word of caution: You must be certain that you answer each destination city correctly! If you do not, then there is a good chance your next destination will not be right either!

1. Your journey is going to start in Los Angeles, California. From there you will proceed 121 miles south on I-5, and you will have arrived in the city of _____.

2. From this city you will proceed east on I-8 until it intersects with I-10, where you turn southeast toward your destination (419 miles altogether), and you will be in the city of _____.

3. From here you go northwest on I-10 to I-17—then proceed north to a total distance of 271 miles, and you will be in the city of _____.

4. From there you proceed in an easterly direction on I-40 a distance of 325 miles, and you will be in the city of _____.

5. The next stop involves taking I-25 south until it intersects with I-10, where you proceed east until the odometer reads 727 miles, and you should now be in the city of _____.

6. Go east on I-10 for 200 miles, and you will now be in the city of _____.

7. From there, you continue east on I-10 for a distance of 365 miles to the city located at the mouth of the mighty Mississippi known as _____.

8. Back on I-10, you "follow the Gulf" as you travel in an easterly direction until you turn south onto I-75. If your total distance traveled with these directions totals 645 miles, you should now be in _____.

9. Continuing another 248 miles southeast on I-75 will find you arriving in the city of _____.

10. Total distance you traveled in this coast-to-coast mission is _____miles.

If you thought that was fun, let's do it again! This time start in Philadelphia and go from the east coast to the west coast.

1. Your journey from Philadelphia begins where I-76 begins, and you travel west a distance of 304 miles where you will be in _____.

2. From there you change routes to I-70 and follow this interstate 360 miles west to the city of _____.

3. The journey then involves finding I-65 and traveling in a northwesterly direction 189 miles to where it lands you in the city of _____.

4. I-94 from this city can be taken in a northwesterly direction a distance of 411 miles to place you in the city of _____.

5. Then you will follow I-35 south 466 miles, and you should be arriving in the city of _____.

6. Go west on I-70 for 616 miles, and you will be in _____.

7. From there, it is a short 100 miles north on I-25 to the next stop in _____.

8. Following I-80 west 457 miles will put you in the city of _____.

9. Continuing on I-80 another 754 miles will place you at your final destination, the city of _____.

10. The total distance traveled on this east coast-to-west coast adventure is _____miles.

You can create another version of this little game with a good road map of the United States. Simply choose a starting point, and then be very careful to make your instructions clear as to the directions you wish your journey to follow. Use a highway distance guide to get the approximate distance to the next city. Create as many stops as you like, but make certain that your friend does the same. When you are both finished, exchange papers and play "Crossing America." Check each other's accuracy when you are finished.

Regions

For a good many years, teachers and authors involved in geographic education have grouped entire areas into regions. The thinking was that students would find similar physical characteristics, a similar political climate, religious and ethnic common ground, as well as a similar economic climate that was shared by an entire area. That line of thinking still remains true today. For this reason *regions* was included as one of the five themes of geography. But the concept also extends beyond that earlier notion to a more global perspective.

Students today are encouraged to compare the similarities (and the differences) experienced by people living in one region with those living elsewhere, perhaps even in another part of the world. The emphasis has shifted to a comparison of how people living in one region satisfy the same basic needs that are common to people living in another region.

Such comparing and organizing of information nurtures students toward a more broad-based understanding of people living in other cultures and should lead them to some rather general conclusions about an area that will stay with them long after they leave the geography classroom. A word of caution should always be used to discourage students from developing conclusions and generalizations that reach the point of becoming stereotypical.

For purposes of studying regions within the United States, the activities found in this material divide the country into these four regions: *Northeastern United States, Southern United States, North Central United States,* and *Western United States.* Down through the years various geographers have included different states in regions that used different classifications and names. However, today the states included in each of the above regions have become fairly standardized.

The states of Alaska and Hawaii are not included in any of the four regions because they are both far different from any of these regions and also because there is another section of this book that focuses on a study of individual states.

Even though studying regions leads to conclusions on similarity on selected criteria, students should understand that time can change a lot of things. Studying those changes in terms of their impact on the present-day condition of a given area is part of the justification for studying regions in geography education.

Name _____

Northeastern United States

To complete the tasks attached to this assignment, you will need to use the outline map of the Northeast that will be provided to you by your teacher.

1. There are 12 states that compose the region known as *northeastern United States.* The outline map shows the entire region including the individual state outlines. See how many you can identify by printing in the two-letter abbreviation of each state. When you are finished, check your accuracy and correct any errors you may have made.

2. Draw in these physical features of the Northeast and properly attach labels where appropriate. Use mountain symbols ᨆᨆ for these mountain ranges: White, Green, Appalachian, Adirondack, Catskills, Pocono. Draw in and label these rivers: Hudson, Delaware, Penobscot, Connecticut, Susquehanna. Label these bays: Chesapeake, Delaware. Label the two Great Lakes that border states in the Northeast. Label also the Allegheny Plateau.

3. The states in the Northeastern part of the United States are deeply rooted in history. This area is where our country had its infant beginnings. Refresh your memory of the 13 original colonies that banded together in 1776 to declare their independence from England. List below the names of those original colonies that are currently a part of this important region.

_____

_____

_____

4. The Northeast has always included some of the most densely populated land in the United States. That much is still true. But the area *is* losing population. In 1900 the area contained almost 30 percent of the nation's population. The 1990 census reported the figure currently to be just over 20 percent. What are some factors that have contributed to this loss of population?

_____

_____

5. In the space below list ten occupations that offer significant job opportunity for the people who live in the Northeast today. You may need to do a bit of research before preparing your list.

1._____   6._____

2._____   7._____

3._____   8._____

4._____   9._____

5._____   10._____

6. Just as every region has its share of problems, so does the Northeast have its own. Find a current news story either from a newspaper or magazine that points to a specific problem that could be considered *regional,* meaning that it has an effect on the entire northeastern United States. Summarize the article in the space below and be prepared to share your thoughts with other members of your class. Be certain to identify the problem, show its regional effect, and include any solutions which have been offered by the writer of the story.

_____

_____

_____

_____

_____

_____

7. Even though the Northeast has lost some of its people, it certainly has not declined in importance to the United States. It has more large cities than any other region in the country. It is the location of our nation's capital. It serves as a port of entry for both raw materials and finished products coming from all over the world. In short, to many who live there, "It's where it's at!" Reflect for a moment about this very important region of the United States. Then in the space below, list several other reasons why you think it is so important to our nation.

_____

_____

_____

_____

_____

_____

_____

_____

_____

_____

_____

_____

_____

_____

The Northeastern United States

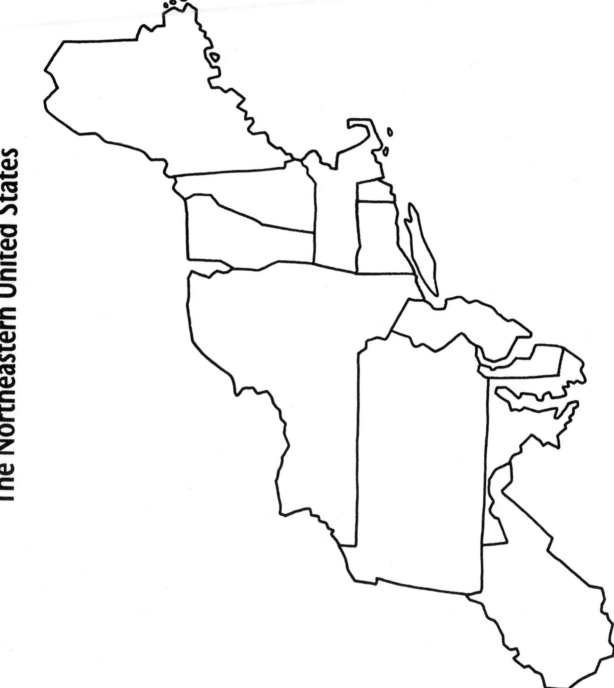

© Frank Schaffer Publications, Inc.

71

FS-10181 Geography . . . USA

Name _____

Southern United States

To complete the tasks attached to this assignment, you will need to use the outline map of the South that will be provided to you by your teacher.

1. There are 12 states that compose the region known as *Southern United States*. The outline map shows the entire region including the outlines of each individual state. See how many you can identify by printing the two-letter abbreviation of each state. When you are finished, check your accuracy and correct any errors.

2. Draw in these physical features of the South and attach labels where appropriate. Use mountain symbols ∧∧∧ for these mountain ranges: Appalachian, Blue Ridge, Great Smoky, Ouachita, Guadalupe. Draw in and label these rivers: Savannah, Tennessee, Rio Grande, Pecos, Colorado, Mississippi, Cumberland, Roanoke, Suwannee, Arkansas, Shenandoah, Chattahoochee. Label these swamps: Everglades, Okefenokee. Label also the Gulf of Mexico and the Piedmont Plateau.

3. The South has also made its contribution to the story of American history. In fact some of the original 13 colonies were part of the South. List the names of those original colonies in the space below.

   _____

   _____

   _____

4. The southern states also played the major role in bringing about America's only war with itself—*The War Between the States*. Do a bit of research on the tragic war, and in the space below list the states that today are a part of the Southern United States but were once a part of the Confederacy. Did all of the states on your outline map join the Confederacy? What other states that allowed slavery refused to join the Confederacy, but remained loyal to the Union?

   _____

   _____

   _____

5. The South has shown significant gains in population in recent years. Certainly the rush to populate the Sunbelt has been in part due to the mild climate found there. But there are other attractions that have brought people to the Southland to live. In the space below list those factors you think have contributed to the growth of the Southern United States.

   _____

   _____

   _____

6. In the space below list ten occupations that offer significant job opportunity for the people who currently live in the South. You may need to do a bit of research before you prepare your list.

1. _____   6. _____

2. _____   7. _____

3. _____   8. _____

4. _____   9. _____

5. _____   10. _____

7. The continued increase in population has brought a great deal of wealth to the South, but it has also presented the region with a number of problems directly related to increased population. Find a current news story that points to one of the problems related to sudden population growth in the South. Summarize the article in the space below and be prepared to share your thoughts with other members of your class. Be certain to identify the problem, show its regional effect on the South, and include any solutions which have been offered by the writer of the story.

_____

_____

_____

_____

_____

_____

8. Most people are pretty much satisfied with where they live. Certainly those who live in the South boast of its mild climate. But sunshine and warm winters are not the sole plus factor associated with living in the South. It has many large cities that have their own unique identity and contribute much to the culture of the United States. What reasons can you think of that will make these growing cities such a viable part of the South?

_____

_____

_____

_____

_____

_____

_____

_____

The Southern United States

North Central United States

To complete the tasks of this assignment, you will need to use the outline map of the North Central States that will be provided to you by your teacher.

1. There are 13 states that compose the region known as *North Central United States.* The outline map shows the entire region including the individual state outlines. See how many you can identify by printing in the two-letter abbreviation of each state. When you are finished, check your accuracy and correct any errors you may have made. Were you able to identify them all?

2. Draw in these physical features of the North Central States and properly attach labels where appropriate. Ozark Plateau, Black Hills, Badlands. Draw in and label these rivers: Mississippi, Missouri, Arkansas, Red, Platte, Ohio, Illinois, Wabash, Wisconsin, Cumberland. Label the four Great Lakes that border on the North Central States.

3. The North Central States have also had their impact on American history. Investigate the *Northwest Territory* and jot down in the space below the five states that were carved out of this area. Also include the history of how it became the Northwest Territory.

   _____

   _____

   _____

4. There are also several states among the North Central States that were once a part of the greatest real estate deal of all time—namely the *Louisiana Purchase.* Find out the name of the president who engineered the deal. Include the name of the seller, the agreed-upon purchase price, and include the names of the North Central States that were carved out of what was once part of the Louisiana Territory.

   _____

   _____

   _____

5. The North Central States are also often referred to as the *Midwest.* In 1900 the Midwest accounted for over 34 percent of the total population in the United States. The 1990 census indicated that those same states could claim only 24 percent of the population. While this may not mean tragedy to the region, it certainly *is* a condition that must be considered. Many companies have left the Midwest to relocate in areas where the tax laws are more favorable, the climate is more favorable, or perhaps for some other reason. Can you think of any other reasons why companies are relocating to other parts of the United States? Also what problems does this present for those who remain? (Place your answer on the back of this sheet.)

6. The Midwest has long been recognized as the "Heartland of America." Find out what this name means both to the Midwest and to the rest of the nation as well.

_____

7. The North Central States lay claim to several of the truly "Great Cities of the United States." Compose a list of those cities that you would include on that list that are located in the North Central States.

_____

_____

_____

8. The North Central States were and remain yet today a major industrial region. In the space below list ten other occupations that offer significant job opportunity for people who live there today. Do a bit of research before you prepare your list.

1._____   6._____

2._____   7._____

3._____   8._____

4._____   9._____

5._____   10._____

9. Just as every region has its share of problems, so do the North Central States. Find a current news story either from a newspaper or magazine that points to a specific problem of the entire region. Summarize the article in the space below and be prepared to share your comments with other members of your class. First identify the problem, then show its regional effect on the area, and include any solutions which have been offered by the writer of the story.

_____

_____

_____

10. Despite what the census numbers may say about it losing population, the North Central States remain home for millions of Americans. It is where they live, where they work, where they play, and where they want to be! In the space below list several reasons why the Midwest remains a region that is so important to our nation.

_____

_____

_____

_____

_____

_____

The North Central United States

Name _____

Western United States

To complete the tasks of this assignment, use the outline map of the Western United States provided to you by your teacher.

1. There are 11 states that compose the region known as the *Western United States*. The outline map shows the entire region including the individual state outlines. See how many you can identify by printing in the two-letter abbreviation of each state. When you have finished, check your accuracy and correct any errors you may have made. Were you able to identify all of them without referring to a map?

2. Draw in these physical features of the Western States and properly attach labels where appropriate. Use mountain symbols 〰 for these mountain ranges: Rocky, Sierra Nevada, Cascade, Coastal Range, Bighorn, Teton, Sangre de Cristo Range. Draw in and label these rivers: Arkansas, South Platte, North Platte, Gunnison, Rio Grande, Colorado, Gila, Sacramento, Snake, Yellowstone, Missouri, Pecos, Columbia, San Joaquin, Humboldt. Draw in and label these other physical features: Puget Sound, Coos Bay, Mojave Desert, Sonoran Desert, Columbia Plateau.

3. The West also has some other points of interest that deserve special note. Locate the following on your map as well: Hoover Dam, Great Salt Lake, Mt. Whitney (highest mountain in the 48 contiguous states), Grand Coulee Dam, Lake Tahoe, Central Valley.

4. No other region in the United States can boast the dynamic population of the West during the past few decades. While it once was known as the "last frontier," that frontier is no longer available in many areas. There remain a lot of wide open spaces in the West, but every year shows more and more people building homes. The spectacular scenery of the mountain states, the mild climate of the Southwest, and the tempered climate of the Pacific Northwest have combined to make it a desirable region for the relocation for thousands of people. In the space below list any other reasons you can think of for the great influx of people that seems to grow greater by the day.

_____

_____

_____

_____

_____

_____

_____

_____

5. California alone accounts for almost 30 million people! That is over 12 percent of the population of the entire United States. Its tremendous growth spurt has created a number of problems, many of which can be traced back to the simple fact that it has too many people for the space and resources available. Investigate the current problems in California and list them in the space provided. Then briefly list some of the ways in which the Golden State has chosen to solve some of those problems.

_____

_____

_____

6. Some of the problems of overpopulation California felt a few years ago are fast becoming problems in some of the other western states. Ranking high on everyone's list is water. Simply stated, there is not enough available water for the needs and desires of the people who live there. Find a current news article that addresses the problem of an inadequate water supply in parts of the West. Summarize the article in the space below and be prepared to share your comments with other members of your class. Be certain to include any solutions that are currently either being implemented or are under consideration.

_____

_____

_____

_____

7. The Pacific Northwest has more rainfall than any other area in the contiguous states, so a lack of water is not a problem there. However, that area of the West has problems of a different nature. Find a recent article that addresses the constant battle between environmentalists and those people whose livelihoods depend on exploiting the resources found there. Again, summarize your article and point to any solutions currently being implemented to solve the dilemma.

_____

_____

_____

_____

_____

_____

_____

_____

_____

_____

The Western United States

Interactions

People are very much affected by their environment. Both physical land forms and climate play a large role in determining the crops that are grown, in the foods that are consumed by the people who live there, in the style of homes people build, in the clothing they wear, even in the activities in which people participate for recreation and relaxation. It might also be said, however, that this statement carried a louder ring of truth 100 years ago than it does today. The technology of today's world has made it possible for man to alter his environment to suit his own needs and desires.

Where it is too dry, we have dammed up the rivers to create reservoirs, then rerouted the flow of water to better serve our needs. We have chopped down virgin forests and natural vegetation to make way for housing projects and shopping malls. We have paved over thousands of square miles of America to give us better highways to travel on and surfaced parking lots for our cars. We have planted crops and built houses in places where crops and houses do not belong—the result being thousands of acres of flooded land. Man has indeed succeeded in altering the environment to better suit his own needs.

But it has not come without a price! The impact of man on his environment is what the theme of interaction is all about. At the risk of casting man in the role of the culprit in this drama, it is nonetheless important for students to analyze some of the trade-offs that come with tampering with nature. That is the entire focus of this material—to get students to think about what has already happened and to be aware of the trade-offs that may occur in the future.

IDENTITY CHALLENGE places students in the role of identifying certain common characteristics that are shared by a significant number of people living in a given area of the United States. They do this by pairing off with another student and choosing an area that is of common interest. Together they create a collage using pictures from magazines or newspapers (or even drawings) to depict those shared characteristics of a given region. Each pair of students should be provided with a 30" x 36" sheet of posterboard. Display the finished posters after students have shared their creations with other members of the class.

ENDANGERED WILDLIFE provides students with some background information on endangered species. Then they are to look at a map of the United States and identify those areas that have the most species of wildlife on the endangered list. During class discussion of the activity, special focus should be given to the last question that has students identifying possible reasons for certain areas of the country being more sensitive than others to the loss of wildlife.

SAVING THE ENDANGERED provides students with a list of over 50 animals that are currently on the endangered list. They are asked to choose one of particular interest and research it. Students identify the habitat of the animal, determine the cause for its being on the endangered list, and tell what is currently being done (if anything) to restore that species to a healthier state. It is important in this assignment for students to share their findings with others. It is also a good idea to avoid duplication in student choices.

WILDERNESS FOR TOMORROW has students evaluating their own thoughts about why the wilderness is so vitally important to us all. They are asked to cite specific reasons for each of eight categories that should be of interest to all of us. Then they make their own rank order of those which they think are most important.

ENVIRONMENTAL VOCABULARY is an activity that tests student knowledge of terms we associate with a study of the environment. Students are asked to create definitions in their own words that show their knowledge of each term. Students also determine whether the term has been coined to identify a detriment to the environment or a condition that is currently helping to save the environment.

Identity Challenge

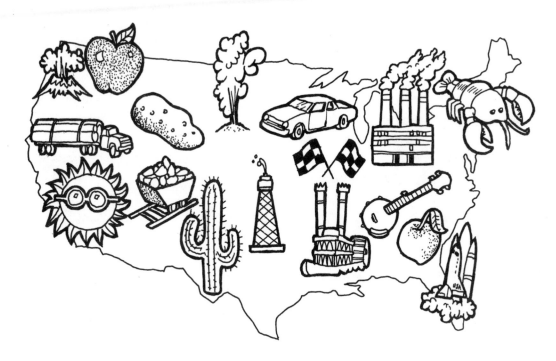

As Americans we all have many common characteristics. For example, we all share a belief in freedom and the ideals that are set forth in the Constitution—our Law of the Land. We also have a strong work ethic that implies hard work will eventually lead to success. Likewise, we share a common belief in the dignity and uniqueness of others and we respect their right to "do their own thing" so long as it is within the law.

But the United States as a nation covers a large area that extends over a wide range of varying climates and physical land features. Because of these differences, we satisfy our basic needs in life in somewhat different ways. For example, seafood is more common on the tables of Americans living in Florida than on the tables of those living in Iowa. We would expect to see more Mexican restaurants in Arizona than in Connecticut. You will have a better chance at seeing homes with mission tile roofs in southern California than in Colorado. You will also see a lot more bighorn sheep in Wyoming than in Louisiana.

So it goes. Different areas of the country have different physical features and climates. The task you and your partner face in this assignment is to choose an area (or a specific state) that is of interest to both of you. Then create a collage on a 30" x 36" sheet of posterboard that will show the "typical" characteristics and qualities of that area or state. Your collage should include pictures of homes, animals, plants, favorite foods of the area, perhaps the landscape itself, recreation that is common to the area, and anything else you feel will help to identify your area or state.

You can use pictures you cut from magazines or newspapers, or you can create your own drawings that will help others to readily identify your collage. The activity below will help you to get the wheels turning. You may need to do a bit of research to make certain that your pictures are correct. When you finish the activity sheet, it should serve as a guide to the subjects of pictures you will either find and cut out or draw yourself. Under no circumstances should you or your partner share your knowledge with other students until you present your collage to the class.

If you do your collage properly, the photos you choose or the drawings you create should make the identify of the area or state you have chosen obvious to others. When you have finished your presentation, attach your activity sheet to the collage with a paper clip and turn it in to your teacher.

Identifying physical features of the land _____

_____

_____

Description of climate including various seasons _____

_____

_____

Animals found in natural habitats _____

_____

_____

Plants and other vegetation common to the area _____

_____

_____

Description of homes that are typical _____

_____

_____

Foods that are favorites because they are common to the area_____

_____

_____

Other identifying characteristics of importance _____

_____

_____

Endangered Wildlife

Before the arrival of man, it is estimated that only one out of a million species died out of natural causes every year. To date, scientists have identified over 1.4 million species of plant and animal life. It is estimated that the earth may currently have over 30 million living species!

With man killing off entire ecosystems on an almost daily basis, tens of thousands of species are lost each year. If that number of losses continues at its current pace, scientists estimate that over one fifth of the planet's life forms will be lost forever within the next 30 years. That will mean millions of species gone forever without ever even having been identified! With their untold value in possible use to cure dread disease and feed starving people, it seems a genuine tragedy that more is not being done to save wildlife.

We all are very aware that man is the culprit who has caused the loss of most of these species. But why? Few would argue that man deliberately sets out to eliminate entire species of plant and animal life. So we come back to the concern about how and why man is such a culprit. The use of pesticides, the pollution of waters and land, and the cutting down of forests are perhaps the most common reasons for the loss of wildlife. It often becomes a simple case of not enough space. When an ecosystem is destroyed, where can it be rebuilt? When man loses his home to a fire or through some other disaster, his home is either rebuilt or he relocates and builds somewhere else. It does not work that way in nature.

In recent years, environmentalists have made us painfully aware of what is happening in nature. Steps have been taken. There are some success stories. Perhaps the most widely publicized is the bald eagle. Overuse of DDT during the 1940s, 1950s, and early 1960s led to the near extinction of the eagle. Since then a wonderful recovery program has brought the bald eagle back to a current status of "threatened," a classification less dangerous than "endangered."

Perhaps this happened because it was our national symbol. Whatever the reason, it shows what can be done when enough people care and the proper steps toward recovery are taken.

Other similar programs are currently under way. The northern spotted owl has drawn a great amount of publicity, and the West Indian manatee also now has at least a chance for survival. Money is being spent and people are becoming educated and thus more involved.

But these programs and other similar efforts are simply not enough. The future of our wildlife rests in the hands of the current and future generations.

The map below shows the location by state of more than 700 plant and animal species currently protected by the Endangered Species Act. The number in each state indicates the number of species protected within that state.

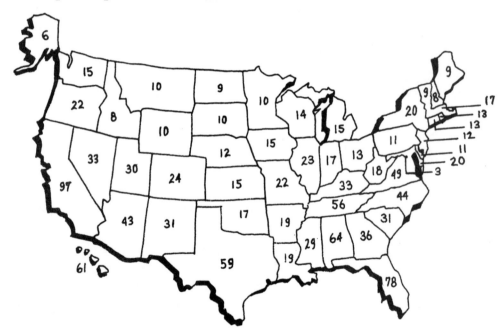

What areas of the United States seem most sensitive to the current loss of wildlife?

_____

Can you think of reasons for the concentration of protected species being located in particular areas of the United States?_____

_____

_____

Saving the Endangered

Since species started dying out in large numbers, man has been labeled the culprit. When we think of the concern that most of us have for saving wildlife, it becomes very difficult to imagine that man could have done so much damage. Perhaps investigating specific species currently on the endangered list will help us to understand why so many species are disappearing every year.

The current list of *most endangered* species in the United States contains the names of over 900 plants and animals. Below are the names of several of the animals on that unfortunate list. Your task is to take a close look at the list and choose one animal that is of interest to you. You will need to do a bit of research to find out *why* that animal is currently on the endangered list and what (if anything) is being done to hopefully preserve the species. Use the accompanying activity sheet to identify your choice and record your findings. Then share your work with other members of your class.

ANIMALS CURRENTLY ON THE ENDANGERED LIST

Hawaiian Monk Seal	Black-Footed Ferret
Laysan Duck	Audubon's Crested Caracara
Eastern Indigo Snake	Stephen's Kangaroo Rat
Jaguarundi	Flattened Musk Turtle
Texas Blind Salamander	Northeastern Beach Tiger Beetle
Thick-Billed Parrot	Northern Spotted Owl
Florida Scrub Jay	Plymouth Redbelly Turtle
Virginia Big-Earred Bat	Red Wolf
Steller's Sea Lion	Wood Bison
Piping Plover	American Burying Beetle
Red-Cockaded Woodpecker	West Indian Manatee
Northern Swift Fox	Stock Island Snail
Gulf Sturgeon	Whooping Crane
Attwater's Prairie Chicken	Shortnose Sturgeon
Houston Toad	New Mexico Ridgenose Rattlesnake
Delta Smelt	Gopher Tortoise
Blue-Tailed Mole Skink	Northern Aplomado Falcon
Koloa Maoli	'Alae 'Ula
Ocelot	Kemp's Ridley Sea Turtle
American Crocodile	Florida Key Deer
Nene Goose	Santa Cruz Long-Toed Salamander
Hawaiian Hoary Bat	Grizzly Bear
California Condor	Wood Stork
Tooth Cave Spider	Hawksbill Sea Turtle
'Io	Cheat Mountain Salamander
Aleutian Canada Goose	Greenback Cutthroat Trout
Devil's Hole Pupfish	'Ae'o

Name _____

Name of endangered animal _____

_____

Physical description of animal _____

_____

_____

_____

Location where animal is currently found_____

_____

_____

Reason(s) for species being endangered _____

_____

_____

_____

_____

Current population (approximate)_____

What is currently being done (or should be!) _____

_____

_____

_____

Wilderness for Tomorrow

When we begin to look at the imprint made by man on his environment, we find certain irresponsible individuals asking the question, "What difference does it make?" Why does it matter if a few forests are cut down? Who cares if a few species are lost? After all, most of the damage done to the environment is not done in the name of destruction, but rather for the sake of progress.

This thoughtless mentality is part of the reason for our jeopardizing the environment in the first place. In recent years environmentalists have made themselves heard, and people are listening. They are also taking positive steps to ensure that further damage is avoided and repair to nature occurs through careful and thoughtful planning.

When we think about the benefits of wilderness, there are many. Below are several categories that cover many of the benefits of wilderness to man. Think about each and jot down a statement or two under each category explaining how saving the wilderness becomes a benefit to man.

Scientific value _____
_____
_____
_____

Commercial value _____
_____
_____
_____

Recreation _____
_____
_____
_____

Name _____

Aesthetic value (beauty)—_____

_____

_____

_____

Historical value _____

_____

_____

_____

Pure water_____

_____

_____

_____

Clean air _____

_____

_____

_____

Educational value _____

_____

_____

_____

Preservation of the species _____

_____

_____

_____

Can you think of any other benefits that derive from preserving nature?

Now go back through your list and place a check mark next to the categories that are most important to you. Be prepared to provide reasons for your choices and share those choices with other members of your class.

Choose one of the benefits that is of particular interest to you and research what is currently being done (and should be done) to ensure that this benefit will continue. Place your findings on the reverse side of this page.

Environmental Vocabulary

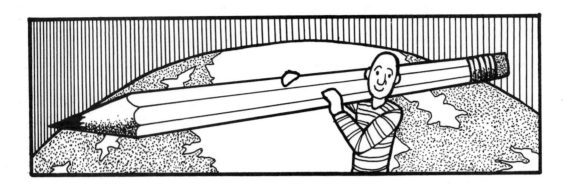

Not so long ago, many of the terms found in the list below were not exactly household words for the average American. But by the early 1960s man began to realize that events and actions were happening to his environment that were creating severe problems. Concerned naturalists began a crusade to educate people about some of man's destructive actions that would lead to an eventual decline of the environment and with it a less desirable quality of life.

The wave of commitment to which most of us are currently involved has today made these terms very much a part of our vocabulary. Show your knowledge of them by jotting down an explanation in your own words that describes the meaning of each. Include comments that describe what man has done to create the problem (if the term is one associated with man) and include any positive steps that are associated with helping to create a more livable environment.

Ozone depletion _____

_____

_____

Greenhouse effect _____

_____

_____

Acid rain _____

_____

_____

Watershed pollution _____

_____

_____

Creative recycling _____

_____

_____

Radon pollution _____

_____

_____

Gridlock _____

_____

_____

Global warming _____

_____

_____

Eating lower on the food chain_____

_____

_____

Overpopulation_____

_____

_____

Ecotourism _____

_____

_____

Earth Day _____

_____

_____

What about you! What are you doing to help to make this planet a better place in which to live? Think about your own contributions and jot them down below and on the reverse side of this page.

_____

_____

_____

_____

_____

Weather

Engaging middle grade students in a study of the geography of the United States should include improving the obvious geographical skills associated with such a discipline. Not so obvious are ideas that are related to a study of weather. There are a number of weather phenomena that occur consistently in certain areas that result in weather patterns, which over a period of time, become the "expected weather" in that area.

The physical geography of an area is in part responsible for the development of some of the weather systems. For this reason, getting students to explore a few of the basics associated with weather, then getting them to draw some concluding generalizations about weather patterns in various areas of the country becomes a clear justification for the inclusion of weather-related ideas in a book focusing on U.S. geography.

HEAT INDEX—COOL IT OR NOT!—Introduce this concept by asking students what they know about the term *heat index*. During the discussion that follows, the term *relative humidity* should be introduced and defined. Students will be better prepared to work on the activity "Cool It! or Not!" if they are armed with the knowledge that the heat index is determined by a combination of temperature and humidity. After students have finished the activity, stimulate an entire-class discussion session. Students who might not fully understand will better grasp the concept if they see the repeated relationship between the temperature our bodies feel and the amount of moisture in the air. It is also advised that you share these suggestions for dealing with heat stress during the group discussion:

HEAT STRESS SAFETY SUGGESTIONS
1. Drink lots of water. Water helps to keep your body from overheating.
2. Avoid getting a sunburn as sunburned skin is more difficult to cool.
3. Wear light-colored clothing that will absorb less heat energy than dark clothes and will help you to stay cool.
4. Spend the hottest times of day in an air-conditioned environment.
5. Avoid engaging in strenuous activities during the time of day when the heat index is highest.

Before assigning either or both of the extended activities, divide students into small groups. They can divide the assignments among themselves and also have the advantage of group interaction in formulating generalizations and conclusions about certain areas of the country. Students should remain in their groups for sharing their findings and conclusions with other groups within the class.

WINDCHILL FACTOR—A CHILLING TALE—This activity should begin with a discussion about watching the weather on television. How many students actually watch the weather forecast every day? How many watch only occasionally? What other media provide forecasts of future weather conditions? Of what value are such forecasts? It is suggested that the teacher initiate a discussion about what students may or may not know about the *windchill factor*. Have they ever heard the term used? When assigning this material, provide an initial example before the entire class (place chart on page 100 on overhead projector) to make certain students understand how to use the chart.

The questions to be answered should be done individually, then student choices shared with other members of the class. Further drill in use of the chart can be accomplished by having the students themselves create similar problems that can be exchanged with other members of the class.

A culmination of this activity involves students developing some general conclusions of their own about the windchill factor. To extend further, have them develop a list of safety rules they feel should be followed when dealing with dangerous windchill factors.

THE DISTANT THUNDER—It is suggested that the activity "The Distant Thunder" be initiated with a discussion of the relationship between thunder and lightning. Depending on the composition and level of sophistication of the interests of students and the desires of the teacher, the presentation can also include a scientific explanation of the cause and relationship between the two. Whether or not this is done, students will have fun with the simple math involved in learning how our senses of sight and sound can be helpful to us during a thunderstorm.

TORNADO ALLEY—Begin the discussion of tornadoes with a review of your school's tornado safety rules. If you live in an area where tornadoes are no threat, share with your students the list of general rules for tornado safety listed below.

TORNADO SAFETY RULES

1. Keep informed of all tornado watches and warnings and be prepared to take cover if a tornado is threatening your area. Your basement is the safest place to be during a tornado. If you do not have a basement, seek shelter in a closet or in a bathroom in the middle of your house. Placing yourself under a heavy piece of furniture will also offer you some protection.
2. Protect your head and eyes from flying objects and pieces of broken glass by wrapping yourself in a blanket or mattress. Stay away from windows.
3. If you live in a mobile home, seek shelter elsewhere. Mobile homes are not structured buildings and can be damaged or picked up by tornadoes. Seek shelter in a solid structured building or in a ditch. You are less likely to be touched by a tornado if you are lying flat in a ditch than if you stay in a mobile home.
4. Do not stay in your car if you see a tornado approaching. Get out of your car immediately and seek shelter in a building or a ditch. Never try to outrun a tornado in your car!
5. If you are in an open field, quickly take cover in a low-lying area such as a ditch. Lie face down covering your head if possible to protect it from flying objects.

After investigating the causes for tornadoes and sharing the activity sheets, have students investigate news reports of a recent tornado. Where did it occur? How much damage was done? Were there any lives lost? What was the rating of the tornado intensity according to the Fujita Scale? If the rating was not provided, how would students rate the tornado according to information they know from the reports?

HURRICANES—TROPICAL TRAGEDY and THE EYE OF THE STORM—Show students the

international symbol used in the Northern Hemisphere to identify a tropical storm by drawing it on the board. Then fill in the oval of your drawing on the board to show them the symbol used to identify a hurricane in the Northern Hemisphere. This should lead into a discussion of just what a hurricane really is. Talk about the difference between a *watch* (issued usually within a 24-36 hour period, meaning that conditions are right for an approaching hurricane) and a *warning* (issued within a 24-hour period, meaning that a hurricane is actually headed for a particular area).

Before getting into the student activities, share with students the safety rules that should be followed when a tropical storm or hurricane warning has been issued. Let them know that Florida's population is currently increasing by over 1,000 new residents each day! With this population boom, it becomes even more important for people to take safety precautions to avoid injury and loss of life. Either read the list of rules to them and discuss together or copy the list for each student for a class discussion during the assignments of the activities.

When forecasters at the National Hurricane Center determine that tropical storm or hurricane force winds will affect a coastal area or a group of islands in a short period of time, they will issue a warning (usually within a 24-hour period). It is extremely important that you observe the following safety rules:

1. Follow the instructions of local officials. Leave the area if you are asked to do so.
2. If you live in a mobile home, go to a shelter.
3. Evacuate coastal areas that may be affected by a storm surge. Head for higher ground immediately!
4. Fill containers with fresh drinking water.
5. Turn your refrigerator temperature control to the coldest setting. This will allow your food to keep longer if you lose electricity in your area.
6. If you are caught in the eye of the hurricane, stay put! Strong winds and heavy rain can return within a matter of minutes!
7. After the storm passes, be on the lookout for downed power lines, especially those that have fallen into water.
8. A storm surge can drive poisonous snakes from their usual habitats. Be on the lookout for them.
9. If your electricity has gone out for any length of time, eat canned food to avoid food poisoning from spoiled food.
10. Beware of weakened tree limbs or sharp objects.
11. Use the telephone only if it is an emergency.

For Further Investigation—The activities below can be used as extension assignments for students who want to investigate further tropical storms and can be assigned either as group work or individual assignments.

Investigate the Intertropical Convergence Zone (ITCZ) and share your findings about what it is and where it is located with other members of your class.

Hurricanes are classified by the intensity and the damage they cause. The Saffir-Simpson Scale categorizes hurricanes on a scale of one to five. Find out how the classification works and explain the basis for each category level. (i.e., What does it mean to experience a Category 3 hurricane as opposed to one classified as a Category 2?

Investigate the current list of names being used to name tropical storms. If the "season" has not yet begun, what will be the name assigned to the first storm? If the hurricane season has already started, what name will be assigned to the next tropical storm? How far down the list of names did the National Weather Service get last year? What was the name assigned to the last storm of the year?

Officials at the National Hurricane Center in Coral Gables, Florida, use a high level of sophistication to gather all the information they can to help predict the intensity of tropical storms, the probable land areas they will cross, and when they will come ashore. Investigate the kinds of information collected and the equipment used to gather that information and share your findings with other members of your class.

WHERE IT'S WET AND WHERE IT'S NOT—When students prepare to examine
the precipitation map and answer the 20 questions, it should be emphasized that they look at a good map of the United States that pinpoints the location of the city found in each question. With that location in mind, students can then visually find the location of that city on their precipitation maps and answer the question correctly.

The general conclusions question at the bottom of the map should be shared with other members of the class. The result of this class sharing should be that students come away with some very general broad-based conclusions about where most of the precipitation occurs in the United States.

. . . AND NOW THE WEATHER—Divide students into pairs for this culminating
activity in which they will actually create and then present to the rest of the class a weather report that is typical for the time of year they have chosen. Make certain you have forecasts from all of the seasons. To add variety to the assignment, assign each group a different major U.S. city to use as their "local base" for their weather presentation. The forecast should include a focus on the local weather as well as an overall presentation of the nation's upcoming weather for the next day or two. Students should be given a copy of the outline map of the United States.

Since watching the weather on television may not be a current priority among your students, suggest that they watch the weather for a few days before they prepare their own forecasts. Better yet, if you have a VCR in your classroom, tape a recent weather show and share it with your students, pointing out the various elements that go into such a presentation.

Cool It or Not!

We all know that on a hot summer day when the temperature soars to 90°, it feels hot! However, the level of your discomfort depends upon your location. It is also true that you can be in the same city experiencing the same exact temperature on different days and yet feel different levels of discomfort. So you may question how that can be possible.

The reason "boils" down to a matter of how much moisture is in the air. When there is little moisture in the air, it becomes easy for evaporation to take place. Perspiration is the body's way of cooling off. If your body becomes warm, you perspire easily if there is little moisture in the air. However if the air is full of moisture, less evaporation of your perspiration can occur and you remain uncomfortable.

The word for this moisture in the air is *humidity*. When there is a lot of moisture in the air, we experience high humidity. The amount is measured in percentage points with the highest being 100 percent. At that level the air is literally saturated with moisture.

How this relates to us depends on a combination of air temperature and humidity. If the temperature is cool, the amount of moisture in the air is not too much of a factor when it comes to our comfort zone. If it is hot and there is high humidity, we are probably uncomfortable. The level of this relationship is expressed in what is called the *heat index*. This term refers to a combination of temperature and humidity and becomes a way of relating to what the apparent temperature feels like to our bodies.

Cool It or Not!

Look closely at the chart. As an example, if the air temperature is 90° and the relative humidity is 90 percent, then the *apparent temperature* makes our bodies feel like it is 120°! On the other hand, if that same 90° occurs on a day when the humidity is only 20 percent, then these conditions would make the apparent temperature feel like about 87°. Do you see how important the amount of moisture in the air is to the way our bodies actually feel?

Look closely at the chart and answer these questions to the closest degree or percentage figure you can calculate from the information presented in the chart.

1._____ What is the apparent temperature when the humidity is 60 percent and the air temperature is 80°?

2._____ What is the apparent temperature when the humidity stands at 40 percent and the air temperature is 90°?

3._____ If the air temperature is 100° and the humidity registers at 50 percent, what is the apparent temperature?

4._____ If the air temperature is 100° and the humidity is only 10 percent, what is the apparent temperature?

5._____ If the apparent temperature is 106° and the relative humidity is 40 percent, at what temperature does the mercury stand?

6._____ If the apparent temperature is 125° and the air temperature stands at 95°, what is the humidity level?

7._____ In terms of the comfort zone, would you rather be where the temperature is 90° and the humidity is 65 percent or where the temperature is 100° and the humidity only 10 percent?

8._____ Under which of these conditions will the body have the most difficulty cooling down—85° at 90 percent humidity or 95° at 30 percent humidity?

What conclusions can you draw about the relationship between temperature, relative humidity, and the heat index?

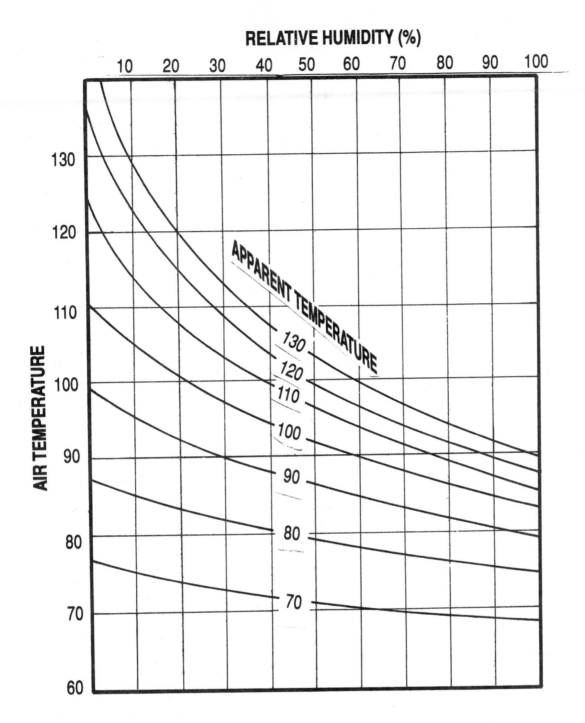

RELATIVE HUMIDITY (%)

APPARENT TEMPERATURE

AIR TEMPERATURE

EXTENDED ACTIVITIES:

Research weather maps and charts and point to specific areas of the United States where the relative humidity is normally low and also find areas where it is typically high. What general conclusions can you draw? (Place your answer on another sheet of paper.)

Look at local weather charts and statistics relating to your own area. At what times of the day is the humidity at its highest and lowest points? During what seasons does the

A Chilling Tale

During the winter months you have probably heard weather forecasters making reference to the *windchill factor*. This terms refers to the apparent temperature your body is perceiving—the combination of both the cold temperature and the speed of the wind—which makes it seem even colder. The explanation goes like this. Your body loses more heat when the wind blows than it does on days with similar temperature but no wind.

Winds also bring about a more rapid evaporation of moisture on your skin. And evaporation of body moisture is nature's way of cooling the body. This cooling is a welcome relief on a hot summer day. But in the winter this loss of moisture makes the body feel even colder!

The relationship of this combination of cold temperature and wind is found in the chart below. A look at the chart will tell you that this combination can quickly reach the point of being dangerous. Look closely at the chart below and answer the questions that follow.

DEGREES FAHRENHEIT

	45	40	35	30	25	20	15	10	5	0	-5	-10	-15	-20	-25	-30	-35	-40	
4 mph	45	40	35	30	25	20	15	10	5	0	-5	-10	-15	-20	-25	-30	-35	-40	4 mph
5 mph	43	37	32	27	22	16	11	6	0	-5	-10	-15	-21	-26	-31	-36	-42	-47	5 mph
10 mph	34	28	22	16	10	3	-3	-9	-15	-22	-27	-34	-40	-46	-52	-58	-64	-71	10 mph
15 mph	29	23	16	9	2	-5	-11	-18	-25	-31	-38	-45	-51	-58	-65	-72	-78	-85	15 mph
20 mph	26	19	12	4	-3	-10	-17	-24	-31	-39	-46	-53	-60	-67	-74	-81	-88	-95	20 mph
25 mph	23	16	8	1	-7	-15	-22	-29	-36	-44	-51	-59	-66	-74	-81	-88	-96	-103	25 mph
30 mph	21	13	6	-2	-10	-18	-25	-33	-41	-49	-56	-64	-71	-79	-86	-93	-101	-109	30 mph
35 mph	20	12	4	-4	-12	-20	-27	-35	-43	-52	-58	-67	-74	-82	-89	-97	-105	-113	35 mph
40 mph	19	11	3	-5	-13	-21	-29	-37	-45	-53	-60	-69	-76	-84	-92	-100	-107	-115	40 mph
45 mph	18	10	2	-6	-14	-22	-30	-38	-45	-54	-62	-70	-78	-85	-93	-102	-109	-117	45 mph

Unpleasant   Frostbite possible   Frostbite likely; outdoor activity becomes dangerous   Exposed flesh will freeze within half a minute for the average person.

1._____ A wind speed of 10 miles per hour with an air temperature of 15° yields a windchill factor of how many degrees?

2._____ When the temperature is 0° and the wind is blowing at a speed of 10 miles per hour, the windchill factor feels like _____ degrees.

3._____ A combination of wind blowing at 20 miles per hour when the mercury stands at -5° provides a windchill factor of _____ degrees.

4._____ If the temperature is -15° and the wind is blowing at 5 miles per hour, what is the windchill factor?

5._____ At what speed is the wind blowing when the chill factor is -40° and the temperature is -15°?

6._____ To what temperature has the mercury dipped when the wind is blowing at 20 miles per hour causing a chill factor of -46°?

7._____ If the wind is blowing at 5 miles per hour, what mercury reading makes it feel like -5°?

8._____ What is the minimum wind speed that makes the wind become a variable in affecting the chill factor?

9._____ When the temperature stands at 20°, at what velocity must the wind be blowing to make frostbite a possibility?

10._____ When the wind blows at a speed of 30 miles per hour, at what temperature does outdoor activity become dangerous?

11._____ When the air temperature reaches -20°, what wind velocity can cause exposed flesh to freeze within half a minute?

12._____ When the air temperature is 20°, what wind speed will make conditions "unpleasant" according to the chart?

13._____ Which of these cities would be most concerned about the windchill factor— Minneapolis, Atlanta, or San Diego?

14._____ In which of these cities would the local climatologist be least likely to mention the windchill factor—New York City, Salt Lake City, or Phoenix?

15._____ Which of these cities would be the most likely candidate to have the lowest windchill factor reading in a given year—Nashville, Philadelphia, or Seattle?

The Distant Thunder

Have you ever wondered about what exactly causes lightning? Those fascinating bolts that light up the sky are nature's way of balancing the difference between positive and negative electrical charges. Actually, lightning is a form of static electricity that is similar to your taking a shirt from the clothes dryer after it has been tossed and turned. As you pull it out, you see tiny sparks. Those sparks resemble the kind of discharge that occurs when lightning bolts are discharged in the sky. There are areas in this country where a single thunderstorm can generate 4,000-5,000 bolts of lightning! The result is the loss of thousands of acres of forested land annually.

A single bolt of lightning can heat the air around it to extremely hot temperatures (estimated to be as high as several thousand degrees). Thunder is the result of the gas molecules absorbing that heat. The change in temperature is so rapid that the expansion of those gas molecules causes the sound we hear as thunder.

You have no doubt seen lightning and curiously wondered just how far it was from you. Sound waves travel approximately one mile in five seconds. To calculate the distance of a lightning bolt, simply start counting immediately when you see the bolt of lightning. One second is the approximate time it takes for you to say "One thousand-one." When you hear the thunder, stop counting. Divide the number to which you counted by five to give you the approximate distance in miles.

So that you will be mentally prepared to calculate such distances the next time you are near a thunderstorm, calculate the following using the above estimation technique:

_____ 1   If you see the lightning and slowly count to five before you hear the thunder, how far are you from the lightning?

_____ 2. If you can count to 10 between the time you see the lightning and hear the thunder, how far are you from the lightning?

_____ 3. If the lightning bolt is approximately 1½ miles from you when it strikes, how far will you count before you hear the thunder?

_____ 4. If your count between lightning and thunder reaches only three, how far away is the lightning?

_____ 5. If you hear the thunder at the same time you see the lightning, what does this tell you?

Tornado Alley

Every year tornadoes do millions of dollars in damage and cause the deaths of many Americans. More tornadoes touch down in the United States than in any other country. The physical features of our nation unfortunately are favorable for the coming together of contrasting air masses. Tornadoes are born out of treacherous thunderstorms when certain conditions are just right. Those conditions occur on the average of 800–1,000 times each year in the United States.

What exactly is a tornado? It is a funnel-shaped cloud that extends downward from a cumulonimbus cloud that contains a rotating column of air. Tornadoes usually begin in the southwestern corner of a thunderstorm and move from a southwesterly to a northeasterly direction. Size may vary, but the average tornado is only about 150 yards in diameter. While the path of a tornado is not nearly as wide as that of a hurricane, the damage left in its wake where it does touch down can be much more severe. The swirling winds inside a tornado are incredible and can reach speeds of over 300 miles per hour!

As with hurricanes, there is a scale that measures the intensity. It is called the Fujita Scale and its basis of comparison is the speed of the tornadic winds. Below is a list of the classifications that define the various intensities.

Fujita Scale of Tornado Intensity

F0	40–72 mph wind	Roof, tree, and sign damage
F1	73–112 mph wind	Trailers flipped and torn apart; cars thrown from roads and sheet metal buildings destroyed
F2	113–157 mph wind	Schools and homes unroofed; some buildings, homes, and schools destroyed; trailers disintegrated
F3	158–206 mph wind	Schools, homes, and businesses have outside walls blown away
F4	207–260 mph wind	Strongly built homes have all interior and exterior walls blown apart; cars thrown several hundred yards
F5	261–318 mph wind	Most homes completely blown away

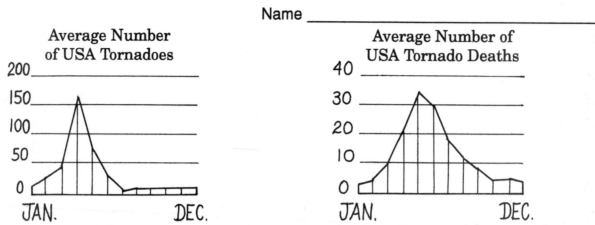

Average Number
of USA Tornadoes

Average Number of
USA Tornado Deaths

What conclusions can you draw about the tornado season in the United States? During what months do most tornadoes occur?

_____

_____

Most tornadoes in the United States occur within an area that extends east of the Rocky Mountains from Texas up through the plains states to the Midwest. Included are also the Great Lakes region and the Ohio River Valley. This main belt of tornadic activity is known as Tornado Alley. There is another area from Florida extending up through the Carolinas that also has frequent tornadoes. While tornadoes can occur anywhere if the conditions are right, they are more likely to occur in these two areas. Using a colored map pencil, outline these two areas on the map below.

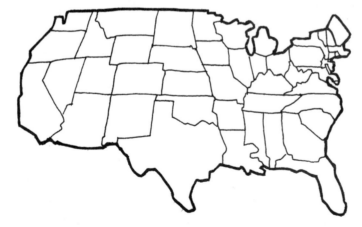

Look at the above map and consider the physical geography of the United States. What effect do you think the geography of the United States has on making conditions favorable for the spawning of tornadoes within these two areas?

Remember, any severe thunderstorm can produce a tornado. Tornadoes can and often do develop without much warning. Always have a safety plan ready to protect yourself against unexpected severe weather. Investigate the safety rules of your school if you live in an area where tornadoes are likely to occur.

Name _____

Tropical Tragedy

Hurricanes are nature's most violent storms. Lives are lost and billions of dollars in damage and destruction are left in their paths every year. To understand better how a hurricane begins, consider the following definitions.

Low pressure is the cause of most storms. A *tropical wave* develops in an area of weak low pressure and usually brings about thunderstorms. If the tropical wave becomes better organized and intense, it can become a *tropical disturbance*. The next most severe category of low pressure systems is called a *tropical storm*. Such storms have sustained winds of 39–73 miles per hour and are accompanied by heavy rain. A tropical storm that accelerates to conditions of sustained winds of 74 miles per hour or greater is a full-blown *hurricane*. The damage caused by hurricanes can be catastrophic.

If the storm develops in the Atlantic Ocean, it is called a hurricane. In the Pacific Ocean, such storms are called *typhoons*. And if they are located in the Indian Ocean or near Australia, these wild and most intense low pressure systems are called *cyclones*.

When a tropical low pressure system reaches the level of being classified a tropical disturbance, it is given a name. There are six lists of names currently used to name tropical storms. Each list has 21 names that start with a name beginning with the letter *A*. Subsequent names begin with letters of the alphabet that continue through to the letter *W* (with the exception of the letters *Q* and *U*. The lists are rotated on a six-year cycle. For example, the list of names used in 1988 was used again in 1994. In these days of equal rights, each list contains the names of both women and men. The names of men were not included on the list until 1979.

Name _____

Below is a list of the names used on that list. Find each name and circle the letter sequence that makes up that name. Names are found in either vertical or horizontal arrangements of letters and can be either forward (as you read them) or in reverse.

Alberto	Debby	Gordon	Joyce	Michael	Patty	Tony
Beryl	Ernesto	Helene	Keith	Nadine	Raphael	Valerie
Chris	Florence	Isaac	Leslie	Oscar	Sandy	William

P R E N I D A N J T Y O O M

A O F N N O D R O G D U N E

M A C A A S I E Y C N D E I

A L L M O C M I C H A E L R

I B Y T T A P X E R S B E E

L E I L O R V K S I S B S L

L R O E N E L E H S A Y L A

I T U T Y R M I F H T V I V

W O E R N E S T O L Y R E B

D N K A L E A H P A R N W O

F L O R E N C E S T I R N O

When a hurricane causes an extraordinary amount of damage and loss of human life, the hurricane's name is retired and is never used again. Do a little research on your own and find out the name of one of these tropical tragedies that caused so much damage that the hurricane's name has been retired.

_____

_____

_____

_____

_____

© Frank Schaffer Publications, Inc.   106

The Eye of the Storm

Look at the diagram of the anatomy of a hurricane to the right. The eye of the hurricane is the calm center. The outer spiral bands are areas of intense rain. As each band passes through an area, it dumps heavy sheets of rain. There is then a brief break between bands; then another passes through. The wind intensifying is a sign that the wall of the hurricane eye is approaching. The eye wall is the most destructive part of the storm.

Once the eye passes through an area, the wind and rain intensify once again as the wall on the opposite side passes through. Conditions then begin to taper off as the outer bands of rain pass through the area. Air pressure begins to fall and the winds begin to die. We sometimes hear the climatologist talk about a hurricane "losing its strength as it goes across land." The reason this happens and the hurricane eventually dies is because there is no evaporation of warm ocean water to refuel the storm.

How do hurricanes begin? Most develop from a cluster of thunderstorms that are born out of a weakened cold front that has moved into a tropical area. Hurricanes usually occur during the months of June through November. September is the most active month for producing hurricanes. The conditions in the latitude belt between 8° and 18° north latitude are most suited to the development of hurricanes. Approximately six tropical storms develop into hurricanes there each year. The averages show that two of those will strike the United States between the gulf coast of Texas and Maine.

Name _____

Look at the map. Which of these cities appears to be vulnerable to hurricanes? Indicate your choices by circling the name of each. To make correct choices you will need first to locate each city on another map to determine if it lies within the vulnerable range of where hurricanes are most likely to strike.

Norfolk	Galveston	Atlantic City
Indianapolis	Seattle	Cape Hatteras
Tampa	Chicago	Phoenix
Los Angeles	Pensacola	Gulfport
New Orleans	Corpus Christi	Minneapolis
San Antonio	Boston	Key West
Miami	Detroit	Kansas City

Develop a general conclusion about when and where hurricanes are most likely to cause damage in the United States.

Where It's Wet and Where It's Not!

On the accompanying page is a map showing the amount in inches of average annual precipitation found in various parts of the United States. These averages are based on many years of keeping records and represent the amount that is expected within a given year. Obviously periods of flooding and drought are exceptions. Look closely at the map and answer the questions that follow.

1. _____ How much rainfall is expected in Indianapolis?
2. _____ What is the annual precipitation in Portland, Oregon?
3. _____ What is the yearly precipitation amount for the Tampa-St. Petersburg area?
4. _____ How much precipitation falls annually in Phoenix?
5. _____ What is the annual rainfall in San Francisco?
6. _____ How much rainfall is expected next year in Minneapolis?
7. _____ What is the annual precipitation amount in Philadelphia?
8. _____ How much precipitation falls annually in New Orleans?
9. _____ What is the yearly precipitation expected in Kansas City?
10. _____ What is the annual precipitation expected in Chicago?
11. _____ How much rain falls each year in San Diego?
12. _____ What is the annual precipitation amount for Atlanta?
13. _____ What is the precipitation expectation for the Dallas-Ft. Worth area?
14. _____ How much precipitation does our nation's capital receive each year?
15. _____ What is the annual precipitation expectation for Los Angeles?
16. _____ How much precipitation can be expected in Nashville?
17. _____ What is the precipitation amount annually for New York City?
18. _____ How much rainfall is expected in Miami?
19. _____ What is the annual precipitation in Cheyenne?
20. _____ What is the annual precipitation expectation for Santa Fe?

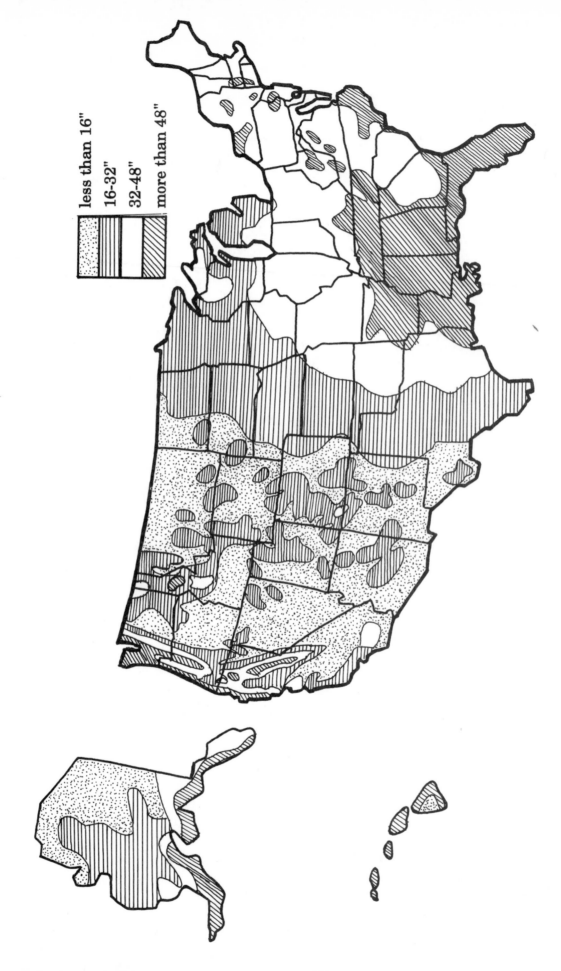

less than 16"

16-32"

32-48"

more than 48"

What general conclusions can you draw about the annual precipitation difference between the East and the West? Are there any other general statements you can make about precipitation amounts?

© Frank Schaffer Publications, Inc.

FS-10181 Geography . . . USA

. . . And Now the Weather

The weather forecasts we see today on television are a far cry from those of the past! Meteorologists make use of colored graphics and dynamic moving overlays to give us a much more colorful weather map that is also a much more accurate picture of what is headed our way. But the basic symbols remain the same. There are a few symbols that define the various fronts and pressure systems that combine to give us our changing day-to-day weather.

Those symbols and what they mean are provided below. Take a close look. Think about how often you hear the meteorologist use them in the daily forecast of future weather patterns.

A *cold front* is the leading edge of a cold air mass that advances into a warm air mass. Cold fronts occur because cold air is denser than warm air.

A *warm front* is the leading edge of a warm air mass that rises over a colder mass of air. Temperatures rise as the warm air replaces the colder air.

A *stationary front* is a boundary that separates two different kinds of air masses. Neither mass has any more influence over the other. It is as though the two air masses are at a standoff.

An *occluded front* involves a cold front overtaking a warm front. Such fronts often occur when a storm is weakening.

H

High pressure systems are associated with sunshine and good weather. The light winds usually blow in a clockwise direction. There is no precipitation associated with high pressure systems.

L

Low pressure systems contain counterclockwise winds that form between a cold and warm front. Such systems are usually associated with storms and precipitation.

Spend some time with your partner finding out why various weather systems occur. Look at weather maps and read the description of the type of weather that is happening in various areas of the country. Then use the outline map of the United States provided to create your own weather forecast. Decide what kind of systems you want to bring specific conditions to certain areas of the nation. Those weather systems should be consistent with the kind of weather that is appropriate for the season you have chosen.

Draw in the symbols on your map. Then prepare a dialogue with your partner that will explain to other members of your class your "future" weather forecast. Explain each system. Include also the predicted high and low temperatures for several major cities throughout the United States. The temperatures you predict should be appropriate for the season and for the weather system that is going to be in that area during the time of your forecast.

Place your map onto an acetate overlay that will allow you to explain it visually to other members of your class.

Using the Outline Maps

The outline maps of each of the 50 states can be used in a variety of ways. Since there are two maps on each page, it is suggested that the teacher first enlarge a desired map to a size that will fill an 8½" x 11" sheet of copy paper. Then reproduce as many times as desired.

The maps may be used for any activity the teacher (or student) may desire, but there are also "facts lists" included for use with each state. Each list includes a list of important cities located within that state. There is also a list of the more important physical features, including mountain ranges, rivers, and other notable land or water features. Finally, there is a short list of the major attractions that bring tourists to that state from elsewhere. In some cases there is also a list of famous historical personalities. In light of a recent study which earmarked travel as the number one employer in 39 of the 50 states, tourism cannot be overemphasized.

If use is made of the facts lists, again it is suggested that the teacher enlarge to a size that will be easy for students to read before reproducing. Of course the teacher may find it more suitable to his or her needs to lift (and add) any desired information and record it on the board. Typically, such lists are used in assignments that require students to pinpoint certain locations, but they can also serve as enrichment assignments for further research on a particular state.

For whatever use may be made of the maps, it is strongly recommended that teachers provide students with as many resources as possible. This means having multiple copies of a good, current atlas and several travel guides. There should also be an abundance of current promotional materials created by the department of tourism within each state. Such materials are free, and the addresses of the state departments of tourism can be found in any current almanac. Simply write a brief letter, addressing your needs and intended use of the material. Better yet, dial their toll-free number. Sometimes it may take two to three weeks for the packet of "freebies" to arrive, so it is a good idea to write or call well in advance of the time when the materials are actually needed.

The study of individual states is often a group activity, but it can also be an entire-class assignment. All students can be assigned to the same state, but perhaps a more desirable format involves each student (or group) working on a different state. A group assignment usually involves extended research in which each member of the group targets a different area of research. The teacher can also place students into smaller groups, assign each student a different state, and students then compare and contrast their various findings.

Other uses requiring further research:

- Pinpoint historic sites.

- Draw in the network of highways that serve that state. Use various colored pencils or markers to distinguish freeways and toll roads from other highways.

- Draw in historic Indian trails or paths used by early settlers.

- Assign students who may have been born (or lived) in other states to research their native states and locate where they have lived. Students who have lived in a number of other states can create an entire packet of state maps that trace their various moves.

- Pinpoint the locations of famous authors, artists, musicians, athletes, and/or entertainers who currently live in the state.

- Pinpoint the birthplaces of the state's famous sons and daughters.

- Show major agricultural products, creating symbols for a map key to represent each product. Then locate them on an outline map.

- Research the origin of cities bearing names derived from a foreign language.

- Show major economic factors, creating symbols of pictures for a key to represent each. Then locate them on an outline map.

- Assign each student two states of their choice and have them contrast and compare the differences between the two.

- Assign students in pairs to research a state in each time zone.

Included are two maps of the entire United States. These maps are used in several activities found throughout the book. One includes the boundaries of each state; the other does not.

ALABAMA

CITIES OF NOTE:

Huntsville	Montgomery
Birmingham	Decatur
Selma	Dothan
Tuscaloosa	Gadsden
Mobile	Florence

PHYSICAL FEATURES:
Rivers: Tallapoosa, Choctawhatchee, Tennessee, Alabama, Chattahoochee, Mobile, Conecuh, Coosa, Pea

ATTRACTIONS:
Russell Cave National Monument
USS Alabama, Horseshoe Bend National Military Park, Lookout Mountain,

NATIONAL FORESTS: Talledega, Tuskegee, Conecuh, William B. Bankhead

NAMES FROM HISTORY:
George Washington Carver, Booker T. Washington, Martin Luther King, Jr., George Wallace, Jesse Owens, William Gorgas, Rosa Parks

ALASKA

CITIES OF NOTE:

Juneau	Fairbanks
Anchorage	Barrow
Valdez	Ketchikan
Nome	Kodiak

PHYSICAL FEATURES:
Mountain Ranges: Brooks, Coast, Alaska, Aleutian, Talkeetna
Other: Yukon River, Arctic Ocean, Gulf of Alaska, Prudhoe Bay, Prince William Sound, Mt. McKinley, Bristol Bay

NATIONAL PARKS:
Gates of the Arctic, Denali, Glacier Bay, Katmai, Kenai Fjords, Kobuk Valley, Wrangell-St. Elias, Lake Clark

OTHER INTERESTS:
Alaska Highway, Trans-Alaska Pipeline, Arctic National Wildlife Refuge, Tongass National Forest, Misty Fjords National Monument

ARIZONA

CITIES OF NOTE:

Phoenix	Tucson
Scottsdale	Tempe
Mesa	Flagstaff
Chandler	Bullhead City
Bisbee	Casa Grande
Yuma	Lake Havasu City

PHYSICAL FEATURES:
Mountain Ranges: Santa Catalina, Rincon, White, Huachuca, Rivers: Colorado, Santa Cruz

NATIONAL PARKS/MONUMENTS:
Parks: Grand Canyon, Petrified Forest, Saguaro
Monuments: Casa Grande Ruins, Pipe Spring, Montezuma Castle, Navajo, Sunset Crater, Chiricahua, Tuzigoot

OTHER ATTRACTIONS:
Arizona-Sonora Desert Museum, Painted Desert, Kitt Peak National Observatory, Biosphere II, Tombstone, Tubac, Hoover Dam

ARKANSAS

CITIES OF NOTE:

Little Rock	El Dorado
Blytheville	Murfreesboro
Jonesboro	Fayetteville
Pine Bluff	Fort Smith
Camden	Russellville

PHYSICAL FEATURES:
Mountains: Ozark, Ouachita
Rivers: Mississippi, Red, Arkansas, White, Buffalo

MAJOR ATTRACTIONS:
Hot Springs National Park
National Forests: Ozark, St. Francis, Ouachita

CALIFORNIA

CITIES OF NOTE:

Los Angeles	San Francisco
San Diego	Oakland
Anaheim	Long Beach
San Jose	Fresno
Sacramento	Stockton
Santa Barbara	Bakersfield

PHYSICAL FEATURES:

Mountains: Coast Range, Sierra Nevada, Cascade Range, Santa Monica

NATIONAL PARKS:

Yosemite, King's Canyon, Lassen Volcanic, Redwood, Sequoia, Channel Islands
National Monuments: Joshua Tree, Lava Beds, Muir Woods, Cabrillo, Death Valley, Pinnacles

MAJOR ATTRACTIONS:

Disneyland, Golden Gate Bridge, Monterey Peninsula, Carmel, Sea World, Universal Studios, Hollywood, Alcatraz Island, Palomar Observatory

COLORADO

CITIES OF NOTE:

Denver	Ft. Collins
Pueblo	Colorado Springs
Boulder	Grand Junction
Loveland	Sterling
Durango	Glenwood Springs

PHYSICAL FEATURES:

Mountains: Rocky Mountains
Rivers: Rio Grande, Colorado, North Platte, South Platte, Arkansas, Gunnison

MAJOR ATTRACTIONS:

National Parks: Rocky Mountain, Mesa Verde
National Monuments: Dinosaur, Colorado, Florissant Fossil Beds, Black Canyon of the Gunnison, Hovenweep, Great Sand Dunes, Trail Ridge Road, Garden of the Gods, Curecanti National Recreation Area, Estes Park

CONNECTICUT

CITIES OF NOTE:

Hartford	Watertown
New Haven	Middletown
Meriden	Bristol
Stamford	Cheshire
Danbury	Manchester
Stratford	New London

PHYSICAL FEATURES:

Taconic Mountains
Rivers: Connecticut, Salmon, Shetucket, Quinebaug

NAMES FROM HISTORY:

Nathan Hale, Thomas Hooker, Samuel Stone, Jonathan Trumbull, Harriet Beecher Stowe, Noah Webster, Benedict Arnold, Samuel Colt

DELAWARE

CITIES OF NOTE:

Dover	Wilmington
Milford	New Castle
Lewes	Odessa
Newark	Arden

PHYSICAL FEATURES:

Rivers: Delaware, Nanticoke, Pocomoke
Other: Chesapeake Bay, Delmarva Peninsula, Piedmont, Atlantic Coastal Plain

ATTRACTIONS:

Slaughter Beach, Bombay Hook National Wildlife Refuge, Brandywine Creek State Park, Delaware Seashore, Pea Patch Island

FLORIDA

CITIES OF NOTE:

Miami	Tampa
Key West	Tallahassee
Sarasota	St. Petersburg
Fort Myers	Jacksonville
Orlando	Pensacola
Bradenton	Palm Beach

PHYSICAL FEATURES:

Swamps: Everglades, Okefenokee
Rivers: Suwannee, Choctawhachee, Perdido, Matanzas

ATTRACTIONS:

National Parks: Biscayne, Everglades
National Monuments: Castillo de San Marcos, Fort Caroline
Other: Disney World, Epcot Center, Universal Studios, Busch Gardens, Sea World, Kennedy Space Center, Cypress Gardens, Weeki Wachee, Canaveral National Seashore, Osceola National Forest

GEORGIA

CITIES OF NOTE:

Atlanta	Macon
Augusta	Marietta
Valdosta	Columbus
Athens	Brunswick
Albany	College Park
Waycross	Rome

PHYSICAL FEATURES:

Blue Ridge Mountains, Stone Mountain
Rivers: Savannah, Chattahoochee, Suwanee, Coosa

MAJOR ATTRACTIONS:

Callaway Gardens, Chattahoochee National Forest, Dogwood Festival, Okefenokee Swamp, Masters Golf Tournament, Stone Mountain Park

NAMES TO REMEMBER:

Jimmy Carter, Eli Whitney, DeSoto, James Oglethorpe, Martin Luther King, Jr., General Sherman

HAWAII

CITIES OF NOTE:

Honolulu	Lahaina
Waipahu	Hana
Lanai City	Waialua
Wailuku	Lihue
Wahiawa	Hilo
Kahului	Kaneohe

MAIN ISLANDS:

Oahu, Hawaii, Maui, Lanai, Kauai, Kahoolawe, Molokai

PHYSICAL FEATURES:

Mountains: Koolau Range, Kamaileunu Ridge

MAJOR ATTRACTIONS:

Pearl Harbor, Diamond Head, Hawaii Volcanoes National Park, Haleakala National Park, Waikiki Beach, Akaka Falls

IDAHO

CITIES OF NOTE:

Boise	Pocatello
Moscow	Twin Falls
Rexburg	Idaho Falls
Lewiston	Weiser
Orofino	Mountain Home

PHYSICAL FEATURES:

Columbia Plateau, Great Basin
Mountains: Salmon River, Sawtooth, Clearwater, Centennial, Northern Rockies, Middle Rockies
Rivers: Snake, Salmon, Priest, Boise

MAJOR ATTRACTIONS:

National Forests: Nez Perce, Clearwater
Other: Shoshone Falls, Hells Canyon, Sawtooth National Recreation Area, Craters of the Moon National Monument

ILLINOIS

CITIES OF NOTE:

Chicago	Springfield
Rockford	Joliet
Champaign	Peoria
Aurora	Galesburg
Moline	Belvidere
Carbondale	Bloomington
Urbana	Rock Island

PHYSICAL FEATURES:

Rivers: Mississippi, Ohio, Illinois, Wabash, Rock, Fox

MAJOR ATTRACTIONS:

Shawnee National Forest, Sears Tower Lincoln's New Salem, Shedd Aquarium, Field Museum of Natural History, Museum of Science and Industry, Adler Planetarium

NAMES FROM HISTORY:

Abraham Lincoln, Ulysses S. Grant, Ronald Reagan

INDIANA

CITIES OF NOTE:

Gary	Indianapolis
Kokomo	Evansville
Lafayette	Bloomington
Terre Haute	South Bend
Fort Wayne	Michigan City
Columbus	Marion

PHYSICAL FEATURES:

Rivers: Wabash, Ohio, White, Kankakee, Tippecanoe, Salamonie, Eel, Maumee
Other: Lake Michigan

MAJOR ATTRACTIONS:

Indianapolis Motor Speedway, Hoosier Dome, Hoosier National Forest, Tippecanoe Battlefield, Indiana Dunes National Lakeshore, New Harmony

IOWA

CITIES OF NOTE:

Des Moines	Iowa City
Davenport	Cedar Rapids
Dubuque	Waterloo
Sioux City	Fort Dodge
Burlington	Marshalltown
Muscatine	Council Bluffs

PHYSICAL FEATURES:

Rivers: Mississippi, Missouri, Des Moines, Skunk, Little Sioux, Iowa, Big Sioux, Raccoon
Lakes: Clear Okoboji, Storm, Spirit, Red Rock Reservoir, Coralville Reservoir

MAJOR ATTRACTIONS:

Amana Colonies, Plum Grove Historical Monument, Effigy Mounds National Monument

KANSAS

CITIES OF NOTE:

Wichita	Kansas City
Manhattan	Topeka
Lawrence	Leavenworth
Hutchinson	Abilene
Emporia	Salina
Pittsburgh	Garden City

PHYSICAL FEATURES:

Rivers: Arkansas, Missouri, Kansas

MAJOR ATTRACTIONS:

Dodge City, Dwight D. Eisenhower Boyhood Home, Indian Reservations (Sac, Fox, Kickapoo, Potawatomi)

NAMES FROM HISTORY:

Dwight D. Eisenhower, Carrie Nation, James Naismith

KENTUCKY

CITIES OF NOTE:

Louisville	Lexington
Frankfort	Hopkinsville
Paducah	Bowling Green
Owensboro	Covington
Henderson	Morehead

PHYSICAL FEATURES:
Rivers: Cumberland, Ohio, Mississippi, Kentucky, Big Sandy
Lakes: Kentucky Lake, Lake Cumberland

MAJOR ATTRACTIONS:
Mammoth Cave National Park, Churchill Downs, Harrodsburg, Cumberland Gap, Jefferson National Forest, Daniel Boone National Forest, Land Between the Lakes, Abraham Lincoln Birthplace National Historic Site

NAMES FROM HISTORY:
Daniel Boone, Jefferson Davis, George Rogers Clark, Kit Carson

LOUISIANA

CITIES OF NOTE:

New Orleans	Baton Rouge
Shreveport	Metairie
Alexandria	Lafayette
Lake Charles	Jonesboro
New Iberia	Houma

PHYSICAL FEATURES:
Rivers: Mississippi, Ouachita, Red, Pearl, Sabine
Other: Lake Pontchartrain, Gulf of Mexico, Delta of Mississippi River

MAJOR ATTRACTIONS:
Kisatchie National Forest, French Quarter, Avery Island, Louisian Purchase Historic Area, Jean Lafitte National Historic Park and Preserve, Mardi Gras

NAMES FROM HISTORY:
DeSoto, Champlain, Louis Armstrong, Napoleon

MAINE

CITIES OF NOTE:

Augusta	Portland
Bangor	Lewiston
Bar Harbor	Rockland
Waterville	Eastport

PHYSICAL FEATURES:
Mountains: White, Saddleback
Rivers: St. John, Penobscot, Pisctaqua
Other: Moosehead Lake, Grand Lake, Penobscot Bay

MAJOR ATTRACTIONS:
Acadia National Park, Shaker Village, Old Orchard Beach, Mount Desert Island, Kennebunk

MARYLAND

CITIES OF NOTE:

Baltimore	College Park
Bethesda	Hagerstown
Annapolis	Frederick
Rockville	Silver Spring
Cambridge	Aberdeen
Salisbury	Essex

PHYSICAL FEATURES:

Rivers: Potomac, Susquehanna, Gunpowder, Patuxent, Patapsco
Other: Chesapeake Bay, Appalachian Mountains

MAJOR ATTRACTIONS:

Fort McHenry, Antietam National Battlefield, Harpers Ferry, U.S. Naval Academy, Susquehanna State Park, Pimlico Race Track

NAMES FROM HISTORY:

Captain John Smith, Francis Scott Key, Charles Mason, Babe Ruth, Edgar Allan Poe

MASSACHUSETTS

CITIES OF NOTE:

Boston	Salem
Worcester	Gloucester
Lexington	Plymouth
Quincy	Wakefield
Springfield	Glouster

PHYSICAL FEATURES:
Rivers: Connecticut, Merrimack, Chicopee, Nashua, Charles, Concord
Other: Cape Cod Peninsula, Massachusetts Bay

MAJOR ATTRACTIONS:
Freedom Trail, Bunker Hill Monument, Walden Pond, Replica of *Mayflower*, House of Seven Gables, USS *Constitution*, Salem

MICHIGAN

CITIES OF NOTE:

Detroit	Lansing
Muskegon	Grand Rapids
Flint	Kalamazoo
Ann Arbor	Saginaw
Bay City	Pontiac
Holland	Dearborn

PHYSICAL FEATURES:
Great Lakes: Michigan, Huron, Superior, Erie
Other: Detroit River

MAJOR ATTRACTIONS:
Isle Royale National Park, Picture Rocks National Lakeshore, Sleeping Bear Dunes National Lakeshore, Mackinac Island, Greenfield Village, Windsor Tunnel, Hiawatha National Forest, Henry Ford Museum,

MINNESOTA

CITIES OF NOTE:

Minneapolis	St. Paul
Duluth	Rochester
St. Cloud	Bloomington
Edina	Moorhead
Austin	Mankato

PHYSICAL FEATURES:
Rivers: Mississippi, St. Croix, Red, Minnesota
Other: Lake Superior, Lake Itasca, Mille Lacs, Leech Lake, Red Lake (Upper and Lower)

MAJOR ATTRACTIONS:
Superior National Forest, Chippewa National Forest, Voyageurs National Park, Grand Portage National Monument, Lindburgh House, Fort Snelling

NAMES FROM HISTORY:
Hubert Humphrey, Walter Mondale, Eugene McCarthy, F. Scott Fitzgerald, Joseph Nicollet

MISSISSIPPI

CITIES OF NOTE:

Jackson	Tupelo
Meridian	Hattiesburg
Gulfport	Biloxi
Vicksburg	Natchez
Cleveland	Pascagoula
Pearl	

PHYSICAL FEATURES:
Rivers: Mississippi, Pascagoula, Tallahatchie, Tennessee, Pearl, Yazoo, Tombigbee, Leaf
Other: Gulf Coastal Plain, Mississippi Delta, Gulf of Mexico

MAJOR ATTRACTIONS:
Gulf Island National Seashore, Holly Springs National Forest, Tombigbee National Forest, Bienville National Forest, Sharkey Delta National Forest, De Soto National Forest

NAMES FROM HISTORY:
DeSoto, LaSalle, Marquette and Joliet, James Meredith, Jefferson Davis

MISSOURI

CITIES OF NOTE:

St. Louis	Jefferson City
Kansas City	Springfield
Columbia	Independence
Joplin	Hannibal
Sedalia	Poplar Bluff
Hannibal	Cape Girardeau

PHYSICAL FEATURES:

Mountains: Ozark Mountains
Rivers: Missouri, Mississippi, Platte, Osage, St. Francis, Salt, Current
Other: Lake of the Ozarks, Mark Twain Lake

MAJOR ATTRACTIONS:

Lake of the Ozarks, Bull Shoals Lake, Mark Twain Lake, Harry Truman Reservoir, Meramec Caverns, Gateway Arch, St. Louis Zoo, Mark Twain Historical Area

MONTANA

CITIES OF NOTE:

Billings	Helena
Butte	Missoula
Great Falls	Bozeman
Anaconda	Cut Bank
Kalispell	Dillon

PHYSICAL FEATURES:

Mountain Ranges: Rocky, Little Belt, Big Belt, Bitterroot, Pioneer, Madison, Purcell, Cabinet, Absaroka
Rivers: Little Bighorn, Missouri, Yellowstone, Gallatin

MAJOR ATTRACTIONS:

Yellowstone National Park, Glacier National Park
National Forests: Flathead, Custer, Lewis and Clark, Kootenai, Beaverhead, Deerlodge
National Monuments: Custer Battlefield, Big Hole National Battlefield

NEBRASKA

CITIES OF NOTE:

Lincoln	Omaha
Hastings	Grand Island
Scottsbluff	Norfolk
Kearney	North Platte
Beatrice	Ogallala

PHYSICAL FEATURES:

Rivers: Missouri, Platte, Elkhorn, Little Blue, Big Blue, White, Loup

MAJOR ATTRACTIONS:

National Forests: Nebraska, Samuel R. McKelvie
Other: De Soto National Wildlife Refuge, Scotts Bluff National Monument, Homestead National Monument, Chimney Rock National Historic Site

NEVADA

CITIES OF NOTE:

Las Vegas	Reno
Elko	Carson City
Sparks	Battle Mountain

PHYSICAL FEATURES:

Mountain Ranges: Sierra Nevada, Toiyabe, Shoshone, Stillwater, Toquima, Excelsior, Clan Alpine, Pancake, Bilk Creek, Shell Creek, Sheep
Rivers: Colorado, Humboldt
Lakes: Lake Mead, Lake Tahoe

MAJOR ATTRACTIONS:

Las Vegas, Hoover Dam, Great Basin National Park, Lehman Caves National Monument, Reno, Lake Tahoe

© Frank Schaffer Publications, Inc.

NEW HAMPSHIRE

CITIES OF NOTE:

Manchester	Berlin
Rochester	Portsmouth
Dover	Lebanon
Concord	Nashua
Keene	Exeter

PHYSICAL FEATURES:

White Mountains, Crescent Range, Ossipee Range
Rivers: Merrimack, Saco, Connecticut, Sugar, Cold, Piscataqua
Other: Lake Winnipesaukee, Hopkinton Lake, Blackwater Reservoir, Atlantic Coastline

MAJOR ATTRACTIONS:

White Mountain National Forest, Hampton Beach, Merrimack Valley, Lake Winnipesaukee

NAMES FROM HISTORY:

John Mason, John Wheelwright, Daniel Webster

NEW JERSEY

CITIES OF NOTE:

Newark	Atlantic City
Trenton	Elizabeth
Hoboken	Jersey City
Camden	Morristown
Ocean City	West Orange
Cape May	East Rutherford
Paterson	Menlo Park

PHYSICAL FEATURES:

Atlantic Coastline
Mountains: Kittatinny Mountains, Scotts Mountains, Hamburg Mountains
Rivers: Hudson, Hackensack, Delaware

MAJOR ATTRACTIONS:

Appalachian Trail, Atlantic City, Morristown National Historic Park, Edison Museum and Laboratory, Bell Laboratories, Great Swamp National Wildlife Refuge, Boardwalk

NAMES FROM HISTORY:

Thomas Edison, Woodrow Wilson, Grover Cleveland, George Carteret, J. L. Berkeley

NEW MEXICO

CITIES OF NOTE:

Albuquerque	Santa Fe
Las Cruces	Roswell
Taos	Los Alamos
Gallup	Portales
Alamogordo	Tucumcari

PHYSICAL FEATURES:

Mountain Ranges: Rocky, Sangre de Cristo, San Andres, Gallinas, Guadalupe, Sacramento, Caballo, Nacimento
Other: Great Plains, Colorado Plateau
Rivers: Pecos, Rio Grande, Gila

MAJOR ATTRACTIONS:

Carlsbad Caverns National Park, Gila National Forest, Anasazi Ruins, Gila Cliff Dwellings, Pecos Pueblos, Zuni Pueblos

NEW YORK

CITIES OF NOTE:

New York City	Albany
Rochester	Buffalo
Syracuse	Utica
Elmira	Poughkeepsie
Newburgh	Schenectady
Binghamton	White Plains

PHYSICAL FEATURES:

Mountain: Adirondack, Catskill
Rivers: Hudson, St. Lawrence, Erie, Niagara, Susquehanna, Delaware, Mohawk
Lakes: Ontario, Erie, Placid, Oneida, Chautauqua, Great Sacandaga
Other: Niagara Falls

MAJOR ATTRACTIONS:

Statue of Liberty, World Trade Center, Empire State Building, Central Park, Radio City Music Hall, Broadway, Long Island, Wall Street, Rockefeller Center, United Nations, Greenwich Village

NORTH CAROLINA

CITIES OF NOTE:

Charlotte	Greensboro
Raleigh	Chapel Hill
Asheville	Winston-Salem
Durham	Fayetteville
High Point	Wilmington
Greenville	Burlington

PHYSICAL FEATURES:
Mountains: Appalachian, Blue Ridge
Rivers: Roanoke, Neuse, Cape Fear,
Catawba, Yadkin
Others: Albemarle Sound, Pamlico Sound,
Atlantic Coastline

MAJOR ATTRACTIONS:
Great Smoky Mountains National Park
National Forests: Pisgah, Croatan,
Uwharrie
Other: Cape Hatteras National Seashore,
Blue Ridge Parkway

NORTH DAKOTA

CITIES OF NOTE:

Bismarck	Fargo
Minot	Grand Forks
Jamestown	Williston
Mandan	Dickinson

PHYSICAL FEATURES:
Rivers: Missouri, Red, Sheyenne, James,
Knife, Cannonball, Little Missouri
Other: Badlands, Great Plains, Red River
Valley, Lake Sakakawea

MAJOR ATTRACTIONS:
Theodore Roosevelt National Park, Little
Missouri National Grassland, International
Peace Garden

OHIO

CITIES OF NOTE:

Columbus	Cleveland
Akron	Toledo
Cincinnati	Youngstown
Bowling Green	Canton
Dayton	Warren

PHYSICAL FEATURES:
Rivers: Ohio, Sandusky, Cuyahoga, Scioto,
Maumee, Vermillion, Little Miami, Great
Miami, Grand
Other: Lake Erie, Sandusky Bay, Grand
Lake-St. Marys

MAJOR ATTRACTIONS:
Wayne National Forest, Pro Football
Hall of Fame, King's Island, Many historical
attractions associated with the eight U.S.
presidents from Ohio

NAMES FROM HISTORY:
U.S. Presidents: Benjamin Harrison, William
Taft, Warren Harding, William McKinley,
Ulysses S. Grant, James Garfield, William
Henry Harrison, Rutherford Hayes

OKLAHOMA

CITIES OF NOTE:

Tulsa	Oklahoma City
Enid	Stillwater
Muskogee	Bartlesville
Norman	Broken Arrow
Miami	Ponca City

PHYSICAL FEATURES:
Mountains: Ouachita, Sans Bois, Kiamichi,
Ozark, Arbuckle, Wichita
Rivers: Red, Arkansas, Cimarron, Washita,
North Canadian, South Canadian
Other: Lake Texoma, Tenkiller Lake, Oologah
Lake, Eufaula Lake

MAJOR ATTRACTIONS:
Ouachita National Forest, Black Kettle
National Grassland, Chickasaw National
Recreation Area, National Cowboy Hall of
Fame, Will Rogers Memorial

OREGON

CITIES OF NOTE:

Salem	Portland
Corvallis	Eugene
Medford	Coos Bay
Astoria	Bend
Pendleton	Ashland

PHYSICAL FEATURES:
Mountain Ranges: Coastal, Cascade, Wallowa, Klamath, Strawberry, Blue
Rivers: Columbia, Hood, Snake, Willamette
Other: Willamette Valley

MAJOR ATTRACTIONS:
Crater Lake National Park, Hells Canyon National Recreation Area
National Forests: Mount Hood, Ochoco, Willamette, Deschutes, Fremont, Siuslaw, Siskiyou
Other: Columbia River Gorge, Oregon Caves National Monument, Pacific Ocean Coastline

PENNSYLVANIA

CITIES OF NOTE:

Philadelphia	Pittsburgh
Allentown	Scranton
Harrisburg	Reading
Bethlehem	Wilkes-Barre
Erie	Johnstown
Hershey	State College

PHYSICAL FEATURES:
Mountains: Allegheny, Blue Ridge, Appalachian, South, Tuscaroa
Rivers: Delaware, Schuylkill, Monongahela, Ohio, Allegheny, Susquehanna
Other: Atlantic Coastal Plain, Piedmont

MAJOR ATTRACTIONS:
Gettysburg National Military Park, Independence Hall, Liberty Bell, Independence National Historic Park, Hawk Mountain Bird Sanctuary, Appalachian Trail, Valley Forge National Historic Park, Allegheny National Forest

NAMES FROM HISTORY:
Benjamin Franklin, William Penn, Betsy Ross, James Buchanan, Edgar Allan Poe

RHODE ISLAND

CITIES OF NOTE:

Providence	Pawtucket
Newport	Woonsocket
Bristol	Cranston
Warwick	

PHYSICAL FEATURES:
Rivers: Providence, Pawtucket, Ponaganset, Seekonk, Woonasquatucket
Other: Rhode Island Sound, Scituate Reservoir, Atlantic Ocean Coastline

MAJOR ATTRACTIONS:
Many historical buildings of Colonial America have been restored, Slater Mill, Cornelius Vanderbilt Estate

SOUTH CAROLINA

CITIES OF NOTE:

Columbia	Charleston
Greenville	Spartanburg
Camden	Clemson
Darlington	Myrtle Beach
Rock Hill	Georgetown

PHYSICAL FEATURES:
Atlantic Coastal Plain, Piedmont, Atlantic Ocean Coastline, Lake Marion, Lake Moultrie, Sassafras Mountain

MAJOR ATTRACTIONS:
National Forests: Francis Marion, Sumter
Other: Hilton Head Island, Myrtle Beach resort area, Fort Moultrie, many homes and mansions and preserved historic sites of Civil War Era

SOUTH DAKOTA

CITIES OF NOTE:

Rapid City	Pierre
Sioux Falls	Mitchell
Aberdeen	Watertown
Huron	Vermillion
Brookings	Yankton

PHYSICAL FEATURES:
Black Hills, Great Plains
Rivers: Missouri, James, Big Sioux,
Cheyenne, Grand, White, Moreau, Lake Oahe

MAJOR ATTRACTIONS:
Badlands National Park, Wind Cave National
Park, Black Hills National Forest, Mount
Rushmore National Memorial, Crazy Horse
Memorial, Jewel Cave National Monument

TENNESSEE

CITIES OF NOTE:

Nashville	Memphis
Chattanooga	Murfreesboro
Knoxville	Clarksville
Jonesborough	Oak Ridge

PHYSICAL FEATURES:
Mountains: Appalachian Mountains, Blue
Ridge Mountains
Rivers: Mississippi, Tennessee, Cumberland

MAJOR ATTRACTIONS:
Great Smoky Mountains National Park,
Graceland, The Hermitage, Grand Ole Opry,
Opryland, Lookout Mountain, Shiloh
National Military Park, The Parthenon,
Cumberland Gap National Historic Park,
Cade's Cove, Gatlinburg, Dollywood

NAMES FROM HISTORY:
Andrew Jackson, James Polk, Andrew
Johnson

TEXAS

CITIES OF NOTE:

Houston	Dallas
Fort Worth	Austin
San Antonio	Galveston
El Paso	Amarillo
Lubbock	Beaumont
Corpus Christi	Huntsville

PHYSICAL FEATURES:
Mountains: Guadalupe Mountains, Chisos
Mountains
Rivers: Rio Grande, Pecos, Red, Colorado,
Canadian

MAJOR ATTRACTIONS:
National Parks: Guadalupe Mountains, Big
Bend
Other: Padre Island National Seashore, The
Alamo, Astrodome, Lyndon B. Johnson Space
Center, Riverwalk

UTAH

CITIES OF NOTE:

Salt Lake City	Provo
Ogden	Logan
Cedar City	Brigham City

PHYSICAL FEATURES:
Rocky Mountains, Uinta Mountains, Wasatch
Range, Great Basin
Rivers: Colorado, Sevier, Weber, Strawberry,
White
Other: Great Basin, Bryce Canyon, Zion
Canyon, Bonneville Salt Flats

MAJOR ATTRACTIONS:
National Parks: Zion, Capitol Reef,
Canyonlands, Bryce Canyon, Arches
National Monuments: Rainbow Bridge,
Dinosaur, Cedar Breaks, Timpanogos Cave,
Mormon Temple, Golden Spike National
Historic Site

VERMONT

CITIES OF NOTE:

Burlington	Montpelier
Middlebury	Barre
Proctor	Brattleboro
Saint Albans	Rutland

PHYSICAL FEATURES:

Mountains: Green, Taconic, Vermont
Piedmont
Rivers: Winooski, White, Black, West,
Connecticut, Batten Kill
Other: Lake Champlain, Vermont Valley,
Champlain Valley

MAJOR ATTRACTIONS:

Green Mountain National Forest, many
beautiful covered bridges, Fort Ticonderoga,
many historical sites

NAMES FROM HISTORY:

Calvin Coolidge, Samuel de Champlain,
Ethan Allen

VIRGINIA

CITIES OF NOTE:

Richmond	Alexandria
Roanoke	Williamsburg
Norfolk	Newport News
Fairfax	Lynchburg
Staunton	Harrisonburg

PHYSICAL FEATURES;

Blue Ridge Mountains, Appalachian Plateau,
Piedmont, Shenandoah Valley, Atlantic
Coastal Plain, Chesapeake Bay
Rivers: Potomac, Shenandoah, York, James,
Rappahannock

MAJOR ATTRACTIONS:

Shenandoah National Park, Blue Ridge
Parkway, Yorktown, Arlington National
Cemetery, Tomb of the Unknown Soldier,
historic Williamsburg, Appomattox Court House

NAMES FROM HISTORY:

John Tyler, Zachary Taylor, Thomas
Jefferson, George Washington, Woodrow
Wilson, James Madison, James Monroe,
William Henry Harrison

WASHINGTON

CITIES OF NOTE:

Seattle	Olympia
Tacoma	Yakima
Spokane	Bellingham
Vancouver	Longview

PHYSICAL FEATURES:

Mountains: Rocky, Coast Range, Cascade
Other: Columbia Plateau, Yakima Valley,
Puget Sound
Rivers: Snake, Columbia, Walla Walla,
Yakima, Spokane

MAJOR ATTRACTIONS:

National Parks: Olympic, Mt. Rainier, North
Cascades
National Forests: Colville, Olympic, Umatilla,
Gifford Pinchot, Okanogan, Wenatchee
Other: Mt. St. Helens, Mt. Rainier, Space
Needle

WEST VIRGINIA

CITIES OF NOTE:

Charleston	Wheeling
Huntington	Morgantown
Parkersburg	Martinsburg
Clarksburg	St. Albans
Weirton	Elkins

PHYSICAL FEATURES:

Mountains: Appalachian, Allegheny, Blue
Ridge
Rivers: Potomac, Monongahela, Ohio, West
Fork, Kanawha

MAJOR ATTRACTIONS:

Harpers Ferry National Historic Park
National Forests: Jefferson, Monongahela,
George Washington—Charles Town Historic
District

WISCONSIN

CITIES OF NOTE:

Milwaukee   Madison
Green Bay   Kenosha
Racine   Oshkosh
Appleton   Wausau
LaCrosse   Eau Claire

PHYSICAL FEATURES:

Rivers: St. Croix, Wisconsin, Mississippi, Fox, Chippewa
Other: Lake Superior Lowlands, Lake Michigan and Lake Superior shorelines

MAJOR ATTRACTIONS:

Wisconsin Dells, Ice Age National Scientific Reserve, Apostle Islands National Lakeshore
National Forests: Nicolet, Chequamegon

WYOMING

CITIES OF NOTE:

Cheyenne   Jackson
Casper   Laramie
Sheridan   Gillette
Cody   Shoshoni
Medicine Bow   Thermopolis

PHYSICAL FEATURES;

Mountains: Rocky, Teton, Wind River, Bighorn, Medicine Bow, Absaroka, Laramie
Rivers: Snake, Yellowstone, Wind, Bighorn, Green, Little Missouri

MAJOR ATTRACTIONS:

National Parks: Yellowstone, Grand Teton
National Monuments: Devils Tower, Fossil Butte
National Recreation Areas: Bighorn Canyon, Flaming Gorge
Other: Old Faithful, Mammoth Hot Springs, Yellowstone Lake, Grand Canyon of the Yellowstone

ALASKA

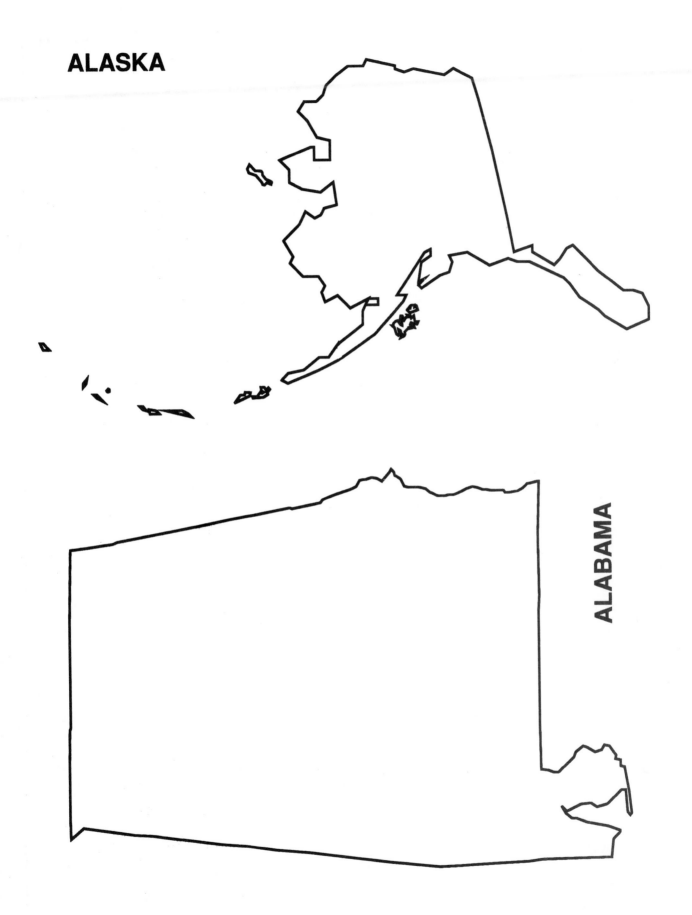

ALABAMA

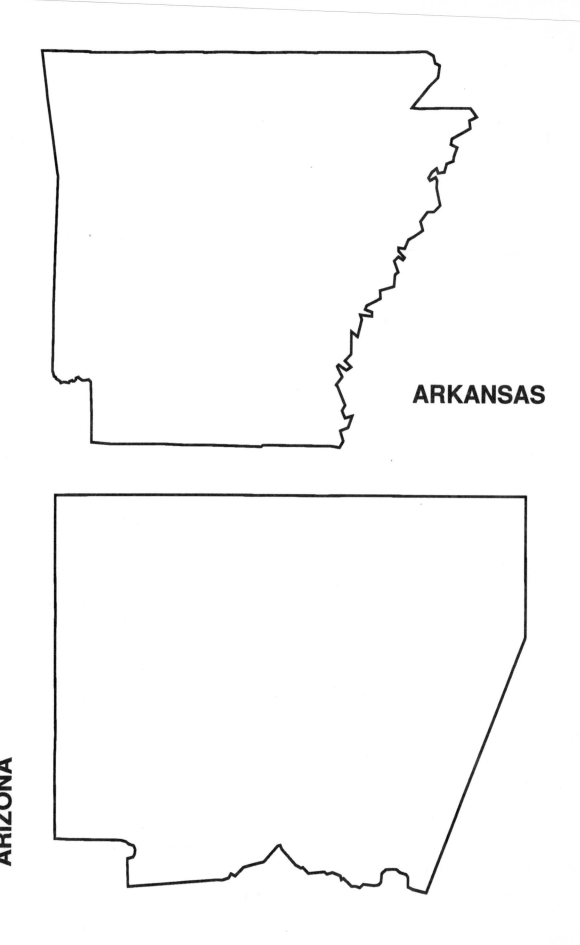

ARKANSAS

ARIZONA

© Frank Schaffer Publications, Inc.

FS-10181 Geography . . . USA

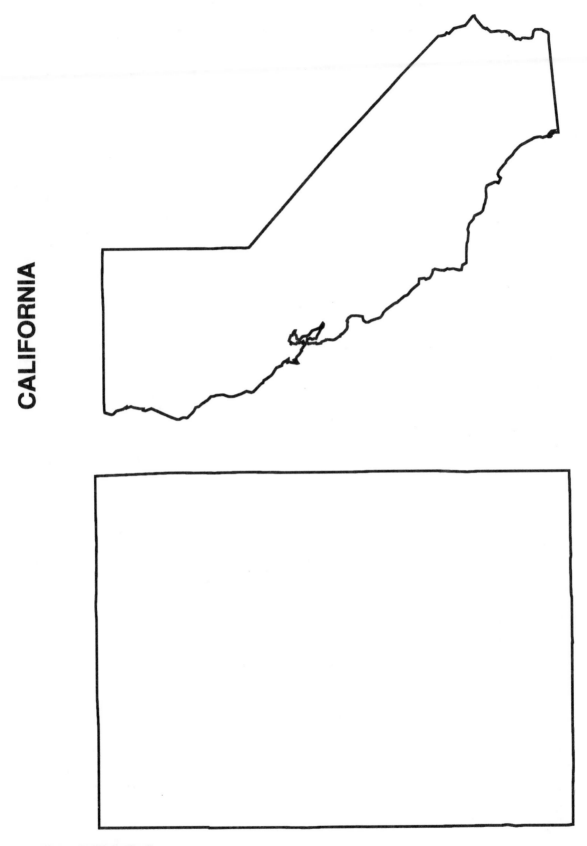

CALIFORNIA

COLORADO

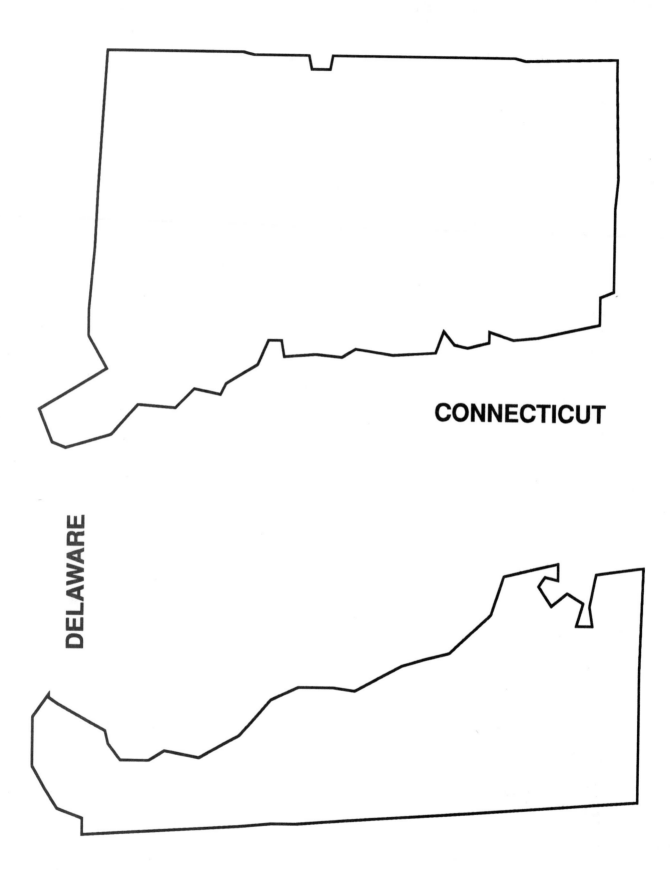

CONNECTICUT

DELAWARE

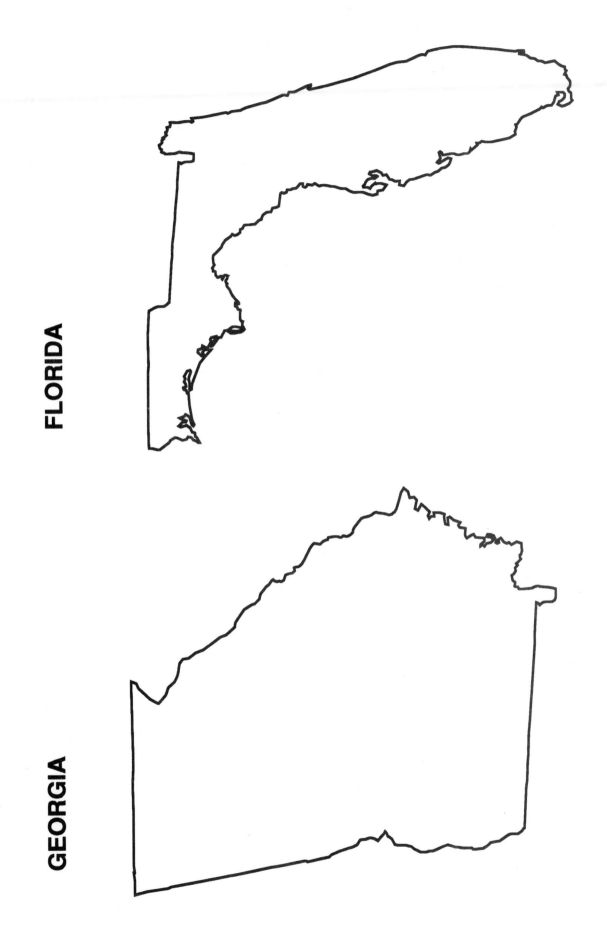

FLORIDA

GEORGIA

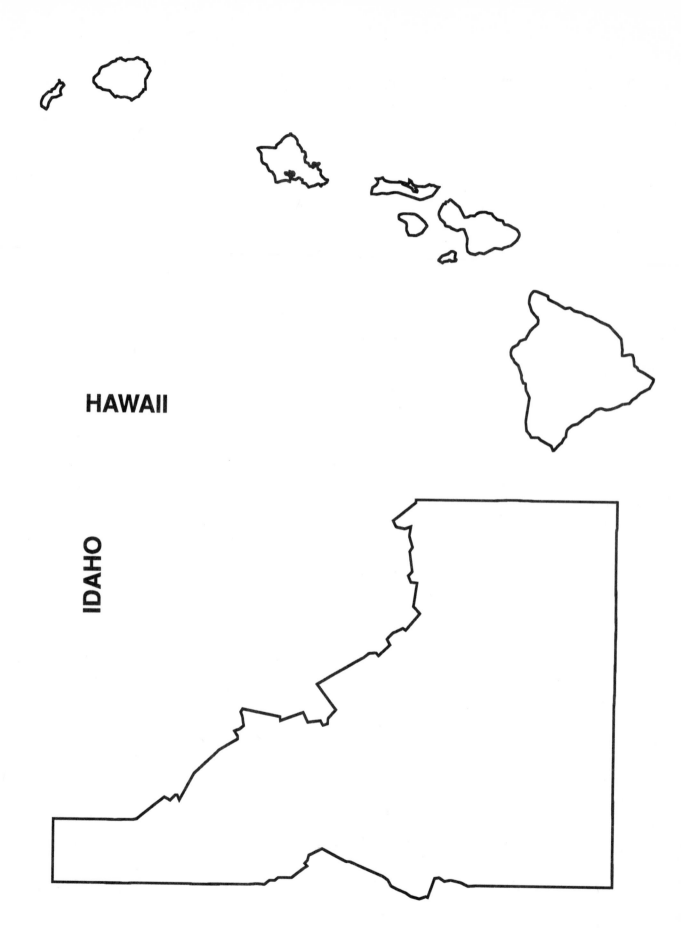

HAWAII

IDAHO

© Frank Schaffer Publications, Inc.

FS-10181 Geography . . . USA

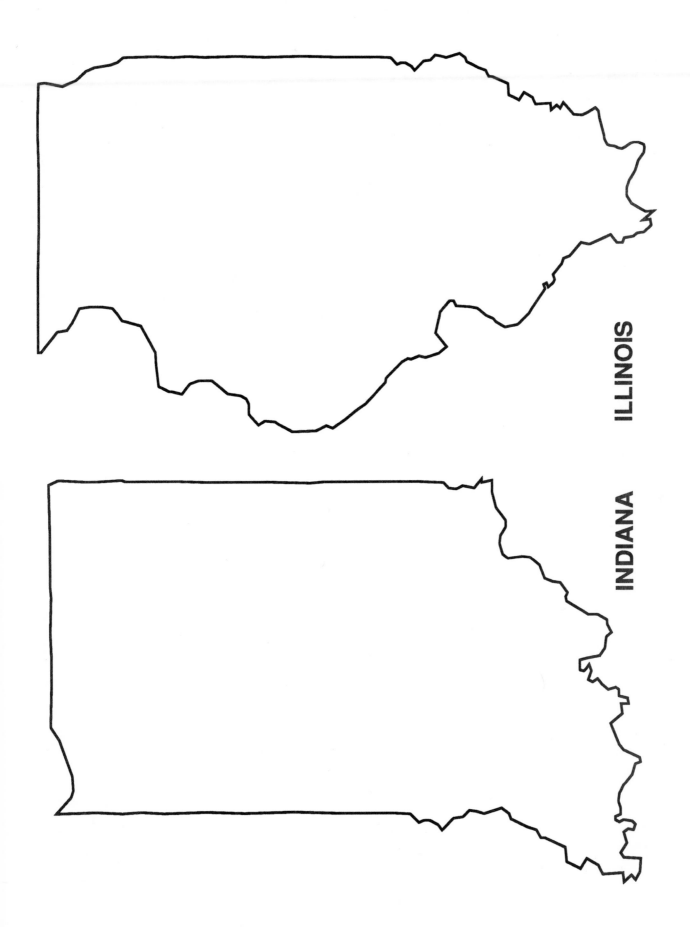

ILLINOIS

INDIANA

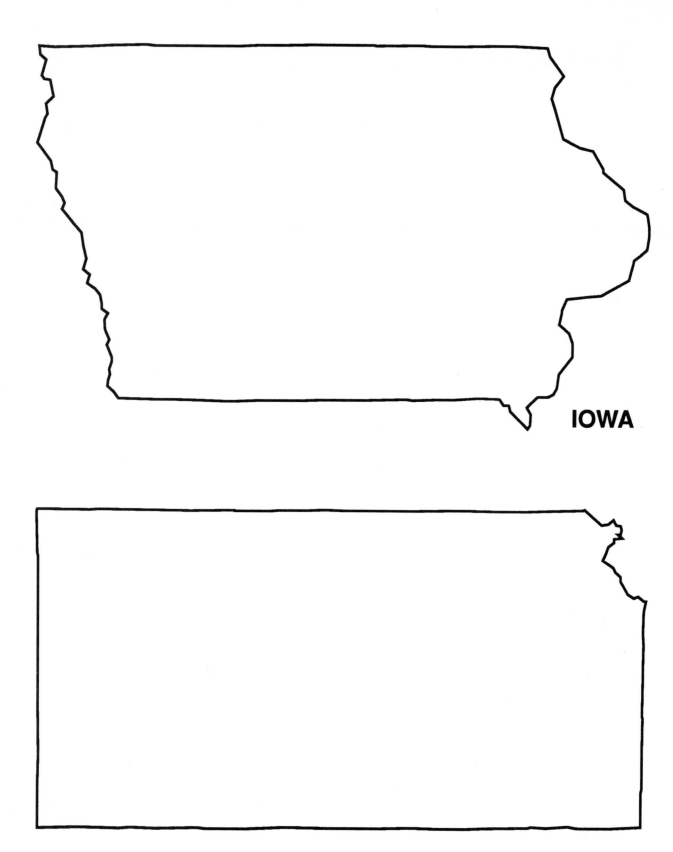

IOWA

KANSAS

© Frank Schaffer Publications, Inc.

FS-10181 Geography . . . USA

KENTUCKY

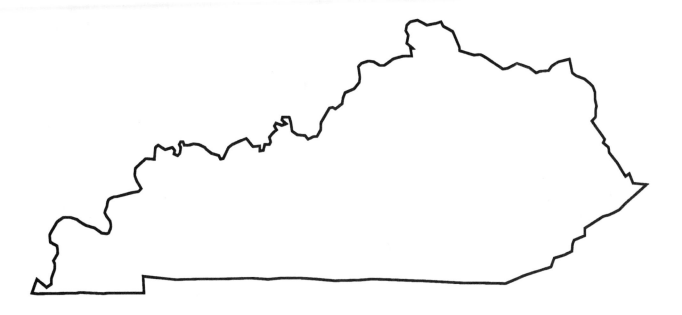

LOUISIANA

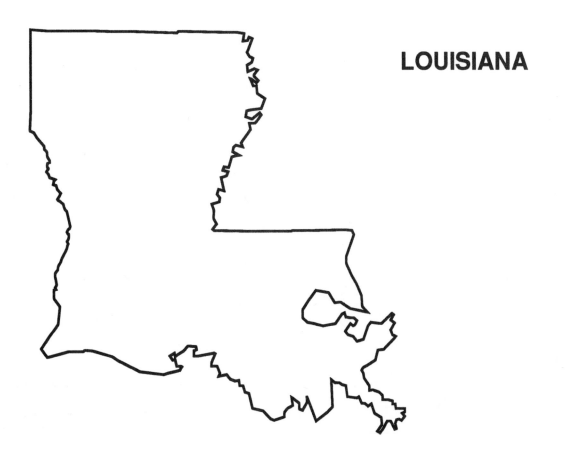

MAINE

MARYLAND

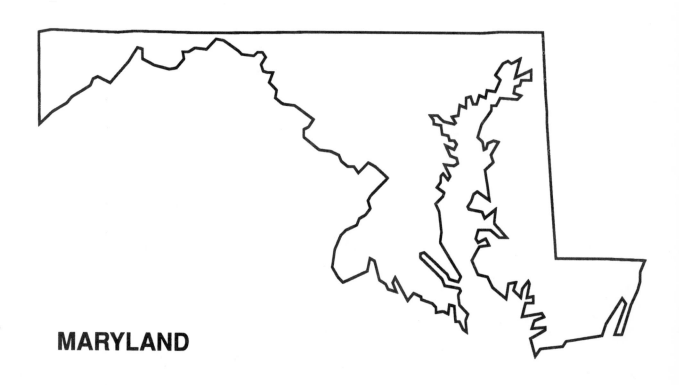

© Frank Schaffer Publications, Inc.

136

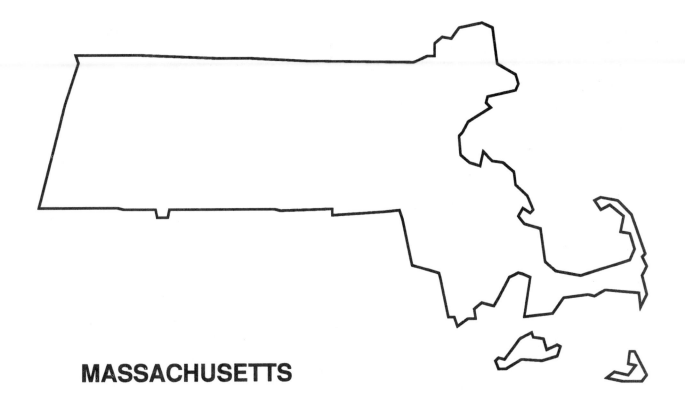

MASSACHUSETTS

MICHIGAN

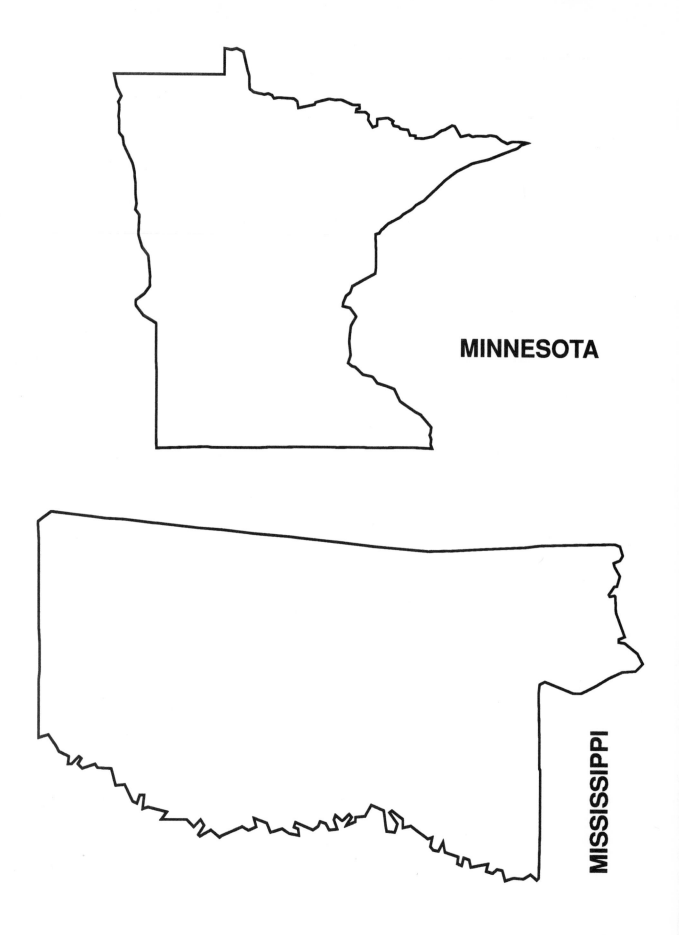

MINNESOTA

MISSISSIPPI

© Frank Schaffer Publications, Inc. 138

MISSOURI

MONTANA

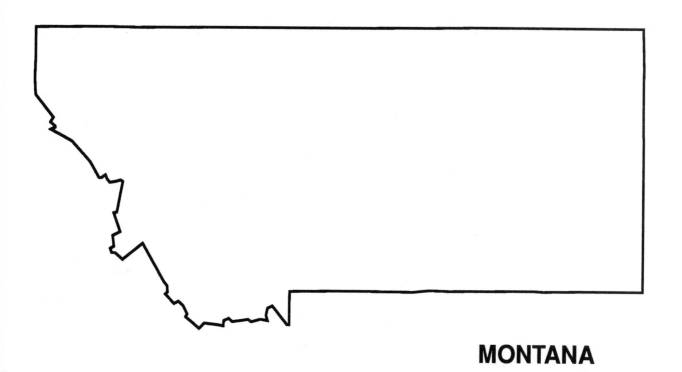

NEBRASKA

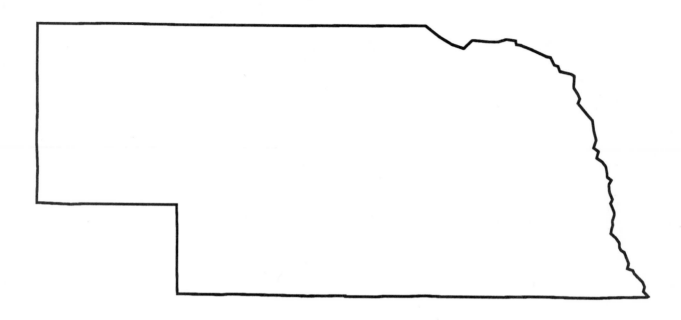

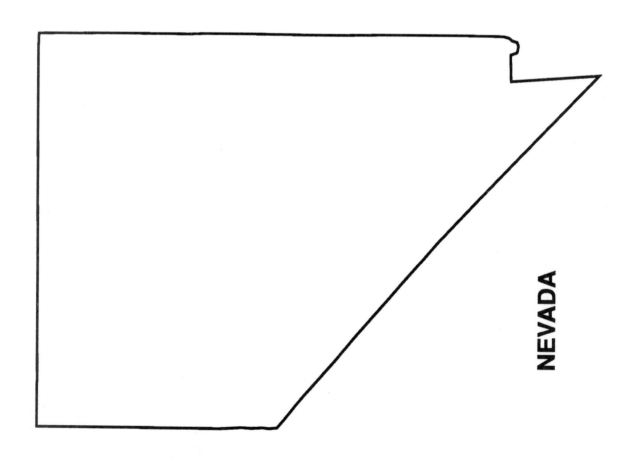

NEVADA

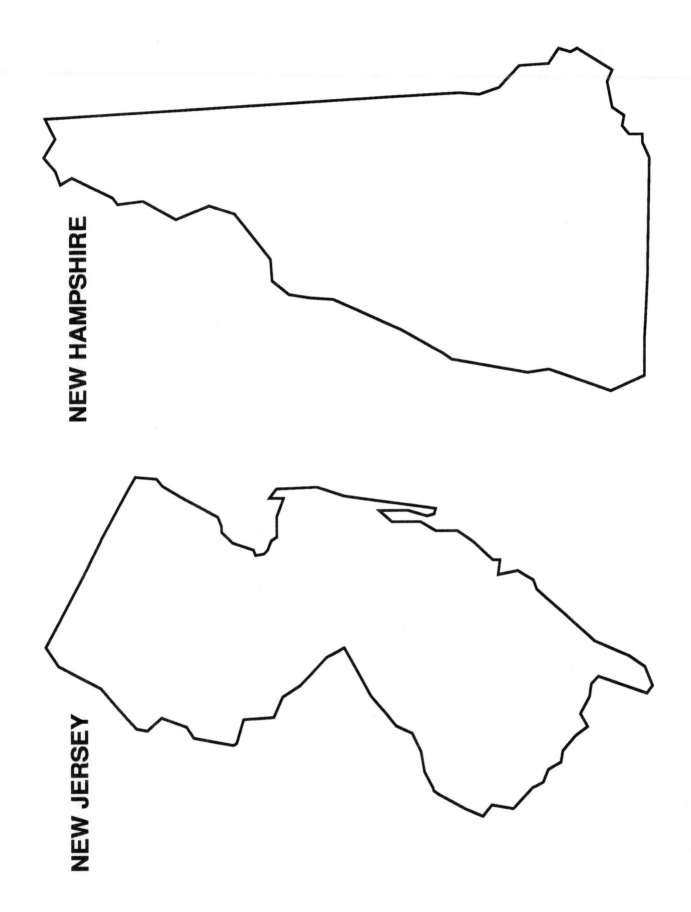

NEW HAMPSHIRE

NEW JERSEY

NEW MEXICO

NEW YORK

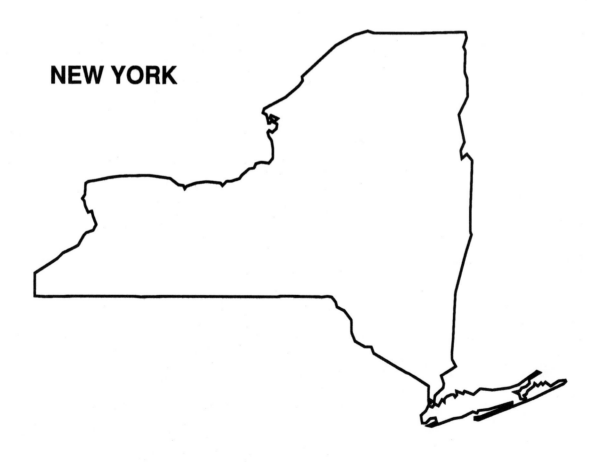

© Frank Schaffer Publications, Inc.

FS-10181 Geography . . . USA

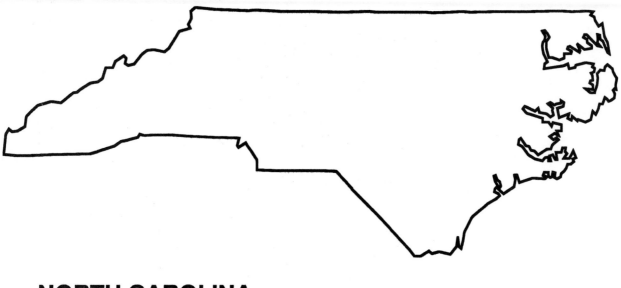

NORTH CAROLINA

NORTH DAKOTA

© Frank Schaffer Publications, Inc. FS-10181 Geography . . . USA

OHIO

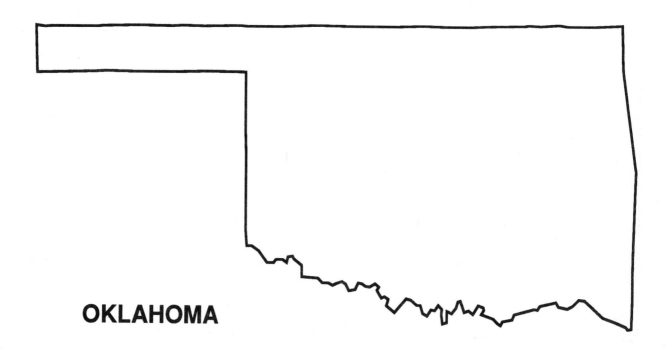

OKLAHOMA

© Frank Schaffer Publications, Inc. 144

OREGON

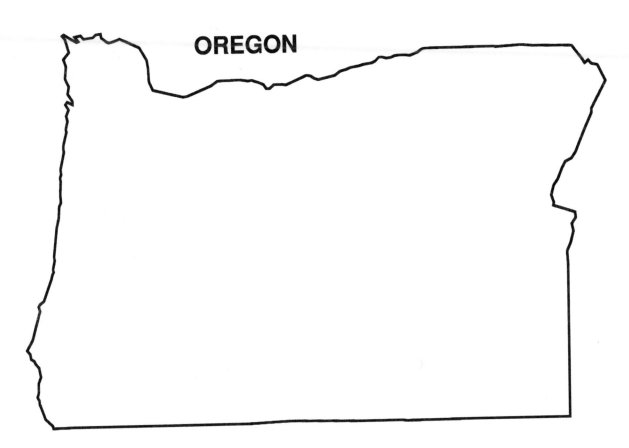

PENNSYLVANIA

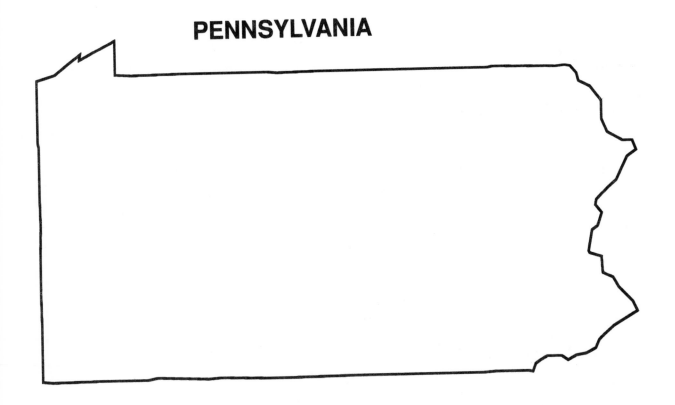

© Frank Schaffer Publications, Inc.

145

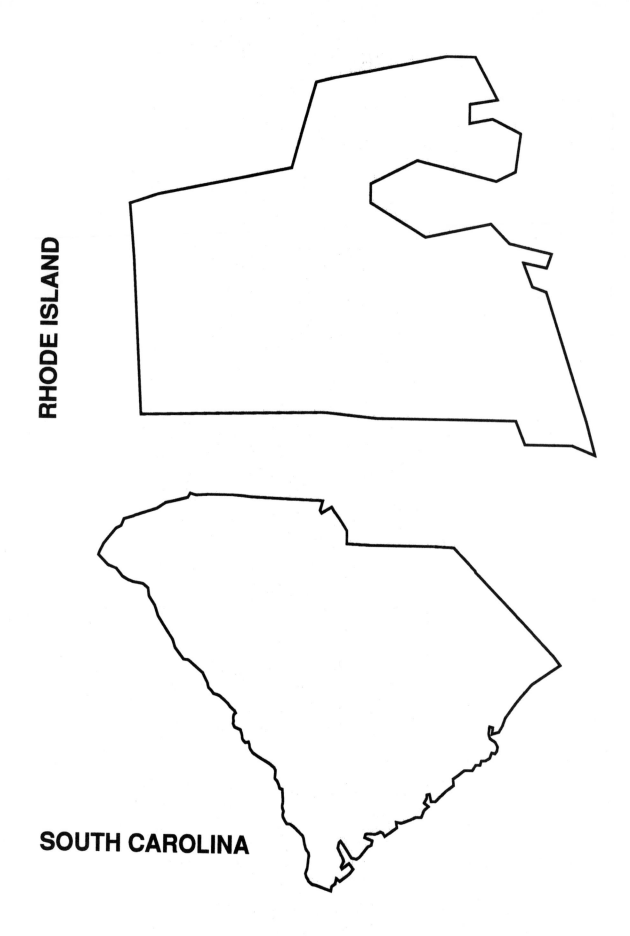

RHODE ISLAND

SOUTH CAROLINA

© Frank Schaffer Publications, Inc.

146

FS-10181 Geography . . . USA

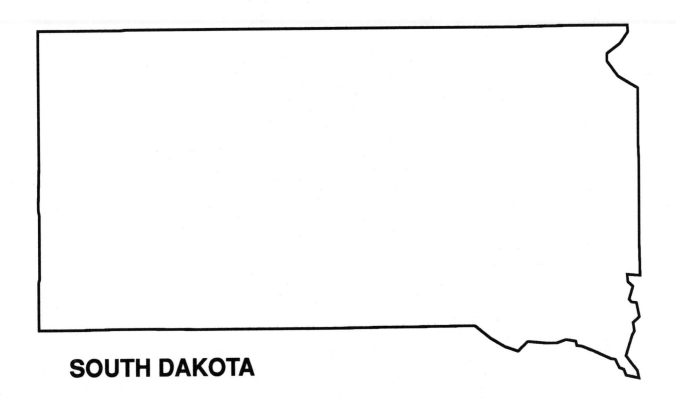

SOUTH DAKOTA

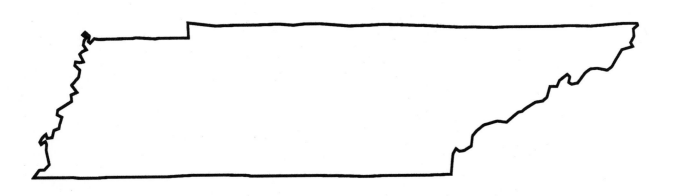

TENNESSEE

© Frank Schaffer Publications, Inc. FS-10181 Geography . . . USA

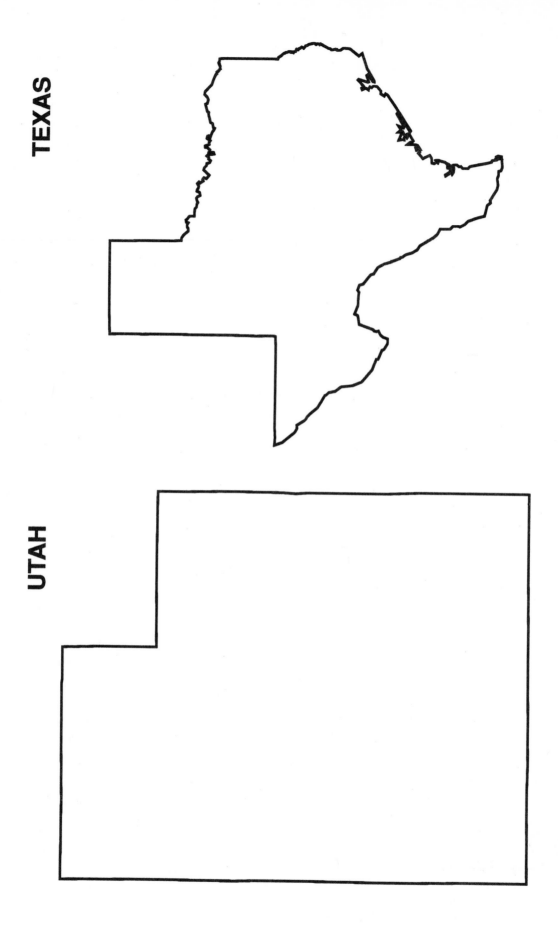

TEXAS

UTAH

© Frank Schaffer Publications, Inc.

FS-10181 Geography . . . USA

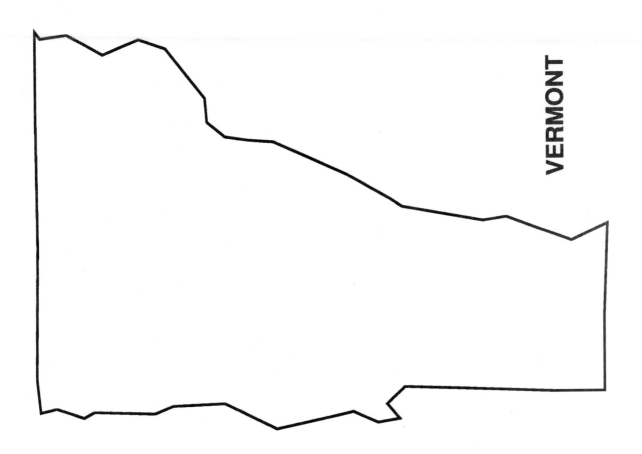

VERMONT

VIRGINIA

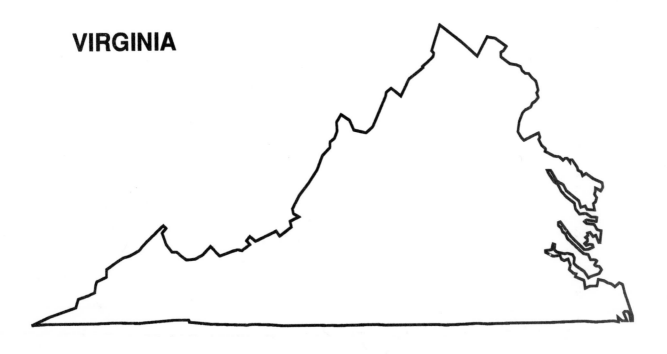

© Frank Schaffer Publications, Inc.

149

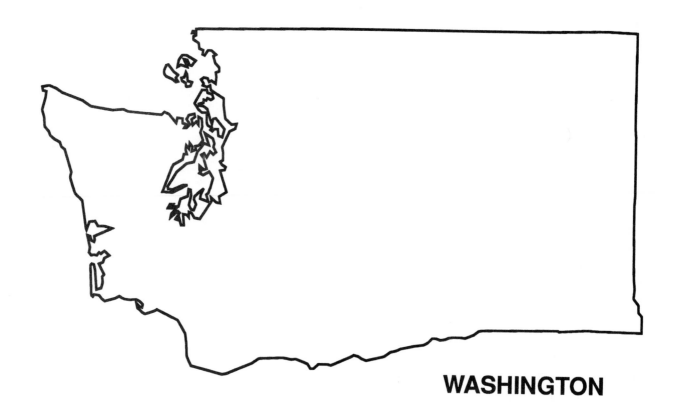

WASHINGTON

WEST VIRGINIA

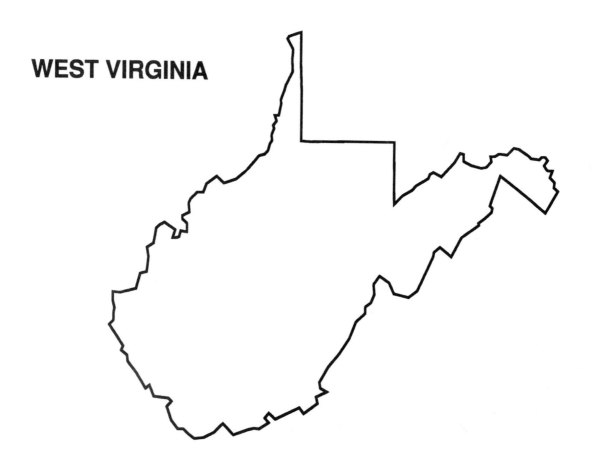

© Frank Schaffer Publications, Inc. 150

WISCONSIN

WYOMING

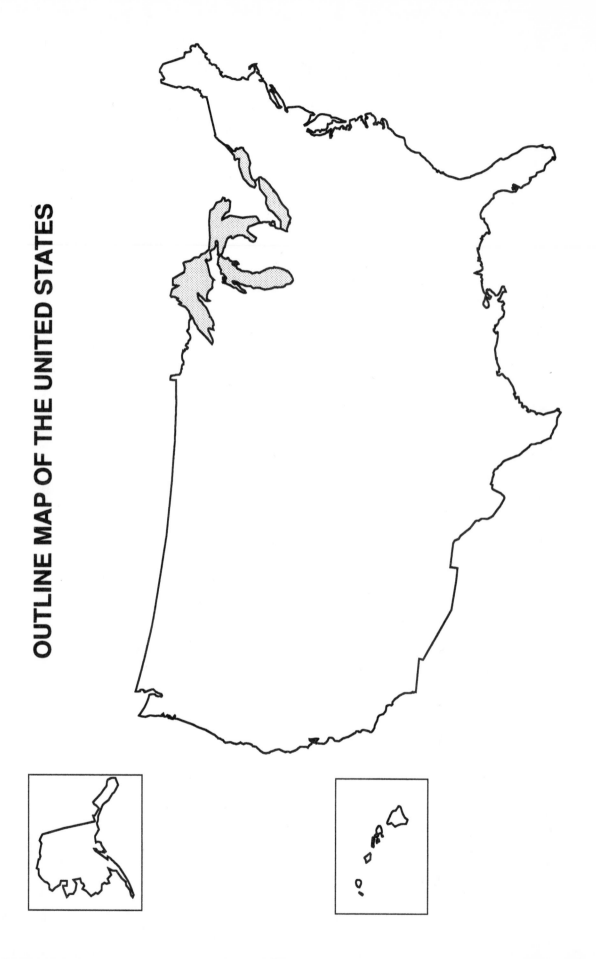

OUTLINE MAP OF THE UNITED STATES

UNITED STATES MAP

© Frank Schaffer Publications, Inc.

FS-10181 Geography . . . USA

Answer Key

Location

1. SW	11. S	21. NW	31. SW
2. NW	12. E	22. SW	32. SW
3. SW	13. N	23. NW	33. NE
4. NE	14. SW	24. NE	34. SW
5. NW	15. NE	25. SW	35. SW
6. SE	16. NE	26. NE	36. NE
7. SW	17. SW	27. NE	37. NW
8. SE	18. SE	28. SE	38. SE
9. SE	19. SE	29. E	39. NE
10. NW	20. SE	30. NE	40. NE

	Direction	Approximate Distance
1.	SE	493 miles
2.	SE	496 miles
3.	W	802 miles
4.	SE	857 miles
5.	NNE	710 miles
6.	WSW	3095 miles
7.	WNW	1883 miles
8.	N	959 miles
9.	SE	552 miles
10.	N	808 miles

1. C-3		5. E-4	
2. B-7		6. D-6	
3. E-7		7. D-2	
4. F-2		8. A-1	

1. 40°N	6. 60°N	11. 50°S
2. 80°N	7. 40°S	12. 10°S
3. 20°S	8. 85°N	13. 50°N
4. 20°N	9. 30°N	14. 84° S
5. 60°S	10. 50°N	15. 70°N

1. west	6. Eastern
2. Eastern	7. 74° West Longitude
3. Western	8. 118° West Longitude
4. east	9. 87° West Longitude
5. Eastern	10. 105° West Longitude

1. Seattle	7. Denver
2. Tampa	8. Honolulu
3. Atlanta	9. Kansas City
4. San Diego	10. Nashville
5. Phoenix	11. Boston
6. Chicago	12. New York City

American League had Chicago in Western Division. It is slightly east of Milwaukee, but the alignments are basically okay geographically. National League had both Atlanta and Cincinnati in the Western Division. Both cities are east of St. Louis and Chicago, which were in the Eastern Division. New alignment in the American League has Cleveland in the Midwest. Cleveland is east of Detroit in the Eastern Division. The National League alignment has Pittsburgh in the Midwest Division. The city of Pittsburgh is east of Atlanta, which was assigned to the Eastern Division. Other answers will vary.

14	Acadia	11	Grand Teton	34	North Cascades
18	Arches	46	Great Basin	4	Olympic
9	Badlands	25	Great Smoky Mt	5	Petrified Forest
31	Big Bend	2	Guadalupe	16	Redwood
40	Biscayne	48	Haleakala	19	Rocky Mountain
26	Bryce Canyon	42	Hawaii Volc.	50	Saguaro
13	Canyonlands	27	Hot Springs	30	Sequoia
21	Capitol Reef	6	Isle Royale	41	Shenandoah
37	Carlsbad Caverns	38	Katmai	33	Theodore Roosevelt
28	Channel Islands	10	Kenai Fjords	49	Virgin Islands
24	Crater Lake	47	Kings Canyon	22	Voyageurs

43	Denali	8	Kobuk Valley	29	Wind Cave
20	Everglades	15	Lake Clark	17	Wrangell-St. Elias
1	Gates of Arctic	23	Lassen Volcanic	36	Yellowstone
35	Glacier Bay	39	Mammoth Cave	44	Yosemite
7	Glacier	3	Mesa Verde	45	Zion
32	Grand Canyon	12	Mt. Ranier		

1. Alaska has 8 parks
2. western
3. 22 states have parks
4. UT, SD, OR, CA, AK, HA, AZ, TX, FL, WA, WY, CO
5. MN, MI, ME, KT, TN, VI, ND, NM, AR, MT
6. Virgin Islands
7. 20 AK-8, CA-6, UT-6
8. 22 states have no national park

1. Kings Canyon		26. Wrangell-St. Elias	
2. Redwood		27. Yosemite	
3. Rocky Mountain		28. Kenai Fjords	
4. Hawaii Volcanoes		29. Gates of the Arctic	
5. Acadia		30. Badlands	
6. Grand Canyon		31. Capitol Reef	
7. Olympia		32. Grand Teton	
8. Zion		33. Lassen Volcanic	
9. Wind Cave		34. Petrified Forest	
10. Sequoia		35. Kobuk Valley	
11. Theodore Roosevelt		36. Biscayne	
12. Shenandoah		37. Everglades	
13. Mt. Ranier		38. Glacier Bay	
14. Isle Royale		39. Channel Islands	
15. Voyageurs		40. Canyonlands	
16. Virgin Islands		41. Great Smoky Mountains	
17. Great Basin		42. Haleakala	
18. Crater Lake		43. Lake Clark	
19. Arches		44. North Cascades	
20. Big Bend		45. Hot Springs	
21. Katmai		46. Denali	
22. Mammoth Cave		47. Carlsbad Caverns	
23. Mesa Verde		48. Bryce Canyon	
24. Glacier		49. Guadalupe Mountains	
25. Yellowstone		50. Saguaro	

Place

Definitions of terms are found in teacher resource notes.

1. j	11. d	21. m
2. o	12. f	22. w
3. v	13. e	23. l
4. p	14. y	24. b
5. i	15. aa	25. s
6. n	16. z	26. a
7. h	17. cc	27. bb
8. t	18. k	28. dd
9. c	19. u	29. q
10. r	20. g	30. x

Answers will vary according to student preference.

Movement

During the past 200 years the population center has shifted from the east coast (where the country had its beginnings) to points farther west. Each census reports a shift even farther west. The shift has also been from more northerly points to a southerly direction. Answers will vary on where students may speculate the center will be 100 years from now, but a good bet would be even further to the west and the south. The current population center (Steelville, Missouri) is southeast from the geographic center (Butte County, South Dakota). The U.S.-Canadian border is considerably longer than the border between the United States and Mexico. The Pacific coastline is longer than the Atlantic coastline.

Representation in Congress
pages 49-51
1. California, 52
2. NY (31), TX (30), FL (23), PA (21)
3. MT, AK, WY, ND, SD, DE, VT
4. 435
5. South, Northeast
6. South, Northeast
7. 571,747

8-10. Answers will vary according to where students live.
11. from Northeast and Midwest to South and West
12. Northeast (89) South (149) Midwest (105) West (92)
13. Northeast (88) South (149) Midwest (105) West (93)

The 25 Largest U.S. Cities
pages 52-55

		Net Gain	% Gain
1.	New York	250,925	3.5
2.	Los Angeles	518,548	17.5
3.	Chicago	-221,346	-7.4
4.	Houston	35,415	2.2
5.	Philadelphia	-102,633	-6.1
6.	San Diego	235,011	26.8
7.	Detroit	-175,394	-14.6
8.	Dallas	103,540	11.5
9.	Phoenix	193,691	24.5
10.	San Antonio	150,053	19.1
11.	San Jose	153,510	24.4
12.	Indianapolis	41,145	5.9
13.	Baltimore	-50,727	-6.4
14.	San Francisco	44,985	6.6
15.	Jacksonville	132,051	24.4
16.	Columbus	68,074	12.1
17.	Milwaukee	-8,124	-1.3
18.	Memphis	-35,833	-5.5
19.	Washington, D.C.	-31,532	-4.9
20.	Boston	11,289	2.0
21.	Seattle	22,413	4.5
22.	El Paso	90,083	21.2
23.	Nashville	55,133	12.1
24.	Cleveland	-68,206	-11.9
25.	New Orleans	-60,989	-10.9

1. 16
2. 9
3. Milwaukee (-1.3%)
4. 10 cities
5. Los Angeles (518,548)
6. San Diego (26.9% gain)
7. Chicago (-221,346)
8. Detroit (-14.6% loss)
9. San Diego, Phoenix, Jacksonville, San Jose, El Paso, San Antonio, Los Angeles, Nashville, Columbus, Dallas
10. Answers will vary, but most of those cities that showed significant gains are located in favorable climates and have many job opportunities.
11. Detroit, Cleveland, New Orleans, Chicago, Baltimore
12. Corporations relocating from area, high crime rates, people desiring a higher quality of life, etc.

Connecting Flights
page 59
1. Denver
2. Boston
3. Las Vegas
4. Dallas-Ft. Worth
5. Philadelphia
6. Seattle
7. Los Angeles
8. St. Louis
9. Tampa
10. Phoenix
11. Atlanta
12. Albuquerque
13. New York City
14. Indianapolis
15. Baltimore
16. Minneapolis-St.Paul
17. Kansas City
18. Detroit
19. Salt Lake City
20. Reno
21. Portland
22. Louisville
23. Tucson
24. Milwaukee
25. La Guardia (NYC)
26. Houston
27. Omaha
28. Oakland
29. Washington, D.C.
30. Orlando

Do You Have the Time?
pages 60-62
1. 3
2. 7:00 p.m.
3. set back
4. 8:00 p.m.
5. Eastern, Central, Mountain, Pacific
6. 2:35 p.m.
7. 9:00 a.m.
8. 5:30 p.m.
9. 9:38 a.m.
10. 5 hours, 45 minutes
11. 1:30 a.m.
12. 3:07 p.m.

The Main Veins of America
pages 64-65
1. east
2. California
3. east/west...Answers will vary.
4. Odd numbered interstates run north/south; even numbered freeways are east/west.

5. I-20
6. I-25
7. I-35
8. I-75, I-81
9. Jacksonville, FL, and Los Angeles, CA
10. I-65
11. I-76
12. San Francisco
13. I-8
14. I-74
15. Chicago
16. Chicago/New Orleans
17. I-5
18. I-64
19. Columbus
20. Albuquerque
21. Detroit
22. I-90
23. I-65, I-69, I-70, I-74
24. I-15
25. I-75
26. I-90
27. I-55
28. I-95
29. I-85 south to Montgomery; then I-65 to New Orleans
30. I-5

Crossing America
pages 66-67
west coast to east coast
1. San Diego
2. Tucson
3. Flagstaff
4. Albuquerque
5. San Antonio
6. Houston
7. New Orleans
8. Tampa
9. Miami
10. Total distance traveled is 3,321 miles.

east coast to west coast
1. Pittsburgh
2. Indianapolis
3. Chicago
4. Minneapolis
5. Kansas City
6. Denver
7. Cheyenne
8. Salt Lake City
9. San Francisco
10. Total distance traveled is 3,657 miles.

Regions

Northeastern United States
pages 69-71
3. Pennsylvania, New York, Massachusetts, New Hampshire, New Jersey, Connecticut, and Rhode Island
4. Among possibilities, corporations have relocated to areas where labor costs are less expensive; people have left areas in favor of less populated areas that are also less expensive, have less crime, often a more favorable climate, and cleaner air. Remaining answers will vary with student response.

Southern United States
pages 72-74
3. Virginia, Delaware, Maryland, North Carolina, South Carolina, and Georgia
4. No, Kentucky and a part of western Virginia (later to become West Virginia) remained loyal to the Union even though they were slave states. Remaining answers will vary with student response.

North Central United States
pages 75-77
3. Ohio, Indiana, Michigan, Illinois, and Wisconsin. The land between the Ohio and Mississippi Rivers was ceded to the U.S. government in the 1780s by the individual states.
4. President Thomas Jefferson engineered the deal with Napoleon of France for a price of $15 million, a cost of about $0.04/acre! Minnesota, North Dakota, South Dakota, Nebraska, Kansas, Iowa, and Missouri were the states from the current North Central states that were once a part of the original purchase.
6. The Midwest is the transportation center of America—where East meets West and North meets South.
7. Among the list should be Chicago, Detroit, Cleveland, Minneapolis-St. Paul, Kansas City, Milwaukee, Indianapolis, Columbus, St. Louis, and Cincinnati. Accept other student choices as well. Remaining answers will vary according to student response. Accept reasonable answers.

Western United States
pages 78-80
Answers for this section will vary according to individual student choices. Accept any reasonable response, but all should be discussed.

Interactions

Endangered Wildlife   pages 85-86

Areas most sensitive to the current loss of wildlife include California, Florida, Hawaii, Alabama, Texas, Arizona, and several other southern states. Most areas are in the Southland where there are more species of wildlife plus considerably greater destruction of habitats and natural environment due to massive construction projects underway there.

Weather

Cool It or Not!   pages 97-98

1. 83°
2. 93°
3. 120°
4. 95°
5. Approximately 97°
6. Approximately 70%
7. 90° at 65% = 105°   100 at 10% = 95°
8. 85° at 90% = 100°   95 at 30% = 95°

Conclusions are that the higher the humidity level becomes on a warm day, the more discomfort will be felt. In areas where the humidity is low (in deserts), the higher temperatures are not as uncomfortable as they would be in areas where the humidity is higher.

A Chilling Tale   pages 100-101

1. -3°
2. -22°
3. -46°
4. -21°
5. 10 mph
6. -5°
7. 0°
8. 5 mph
9. 10 mph
10. 10°
11. 20 mph
12. 10 mph
13. Minneapolis
14. Phoenix
15. Philadelphia

The Distant Thunder   page 102

1. 1 mile
2. 2 miles
3. 7-8 seconds
4. 3/5 mile
5. The lightning is very close!

Tornado Alley   pages 103-104

Most of the tornadoes occur during the months of March, April, May, and June. The peak month is April. The physical geography of the United States is well-suited to the coming together of vastly different air masses. Polar air masses coming out of Canada clash with tropical air from either the Gulf of Mexico or the dry Southwest, thus causing rapid changes.

Tropical Tragedy   pages 105-106

The Eye of the Storm   pages 107-108

Cities vulnerable to hurricanes from the list on page 108 are Norfolk, Indianapolis, New Orleans, Miami, Galveston, Pensacola, Corpus Christi, Boston, Atlantic City, Cape Hatteras, Gulfport, Key West

Where It's Wet and Where It's Not!   page 109

1. 32"-48"
2. more than 48"
3. more than 48"
4. less than 16"
5. 32'-48"
6. 16"-32"
7. 32"-48"
8. more than 48"
9. 32'-48"
10. 32"-48"
11. less than 16"
12. 32"-48"
13. 32"-48"
14. 32"-48"
15. 16"-32"
16. more than 48"
17. more than 48"
18. more than 48"
19. less than 16"
20. 16"-32"

Except for the Pacific Northwest, most places from the Western Plains to the Pacific Ocean are drier than areas in the East. There is also a lot of rainfall near and around the Gulf of Mexico.

© Frank Schaffer Publications, Inc.

FS-10181 Geography . . . USA